# IMAGINATIVE
# SMALL
# GARDENS

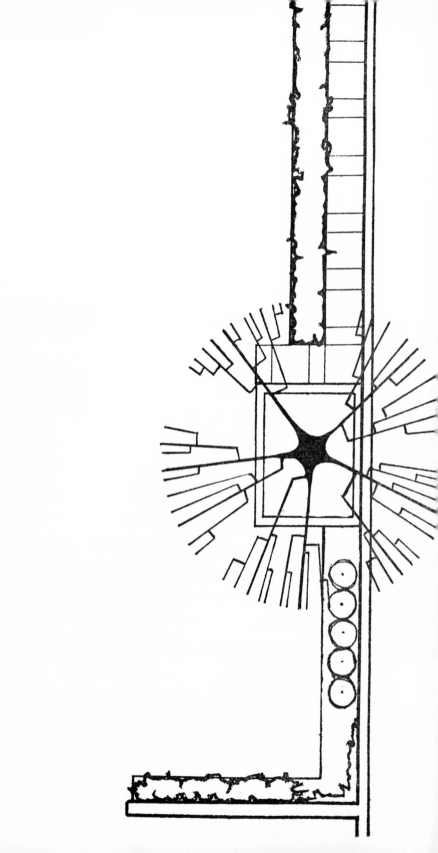

# IMAGINATIVE SMALL GARDENS

by Nancy Grasby

published by Hearthside Press, Inc.
118 East 28th St., New York 16

Unless otherwise stated, designs
and drawings are by the author.

# CONTENTS

## Drawings

## Plates

## TO LESTER ROWNTREE

I am indebted to many persons for help in presenting this book. I especially wish to thank Landscape Architects Dina G. Bauman, Mary Deputy Cattell, John Collyer, John Eyerman, Elizabeth Howerton, Beulah and Harry Klein, Roberta Lord, Margherita Tarr, Luciano Miceli, Nelva Weber and J. D. Zachariah, and Architect Owen A. Luckenbach.

A questionnaire addressed to officers of landscape design schools of the National Council of State Garden Clubs and State Garden Club members brought helpful comment from Mrs. Milton R. Bell (California), Eleanore Benander, L.A. (Rhode Island), Mrs. J. R. Bennett (North Carolina), Mrs. William J. Bullough (Utah), Mrs. Glenn D. Chartier (Kansas), Mrs. George Doolittle (New Mexico), Mrs. James Durden (Alabama), Mrs. A. P. Durfey (Mississippi), Anton S. Horn (University of Idaho), Hubert B. Owens (Department of Landscape Architecture, University of Georgia), Mrs. Gary Paschal (South Carolina), Mrs. Gerald J. Pierce (Virginia), and Mrs. Joseph M. Wallace (Indiana).

Others who responded generously to requests for information were Associate Professor Ronald Taven (University of Missouri), Harvey F. Tate (University of Arizona), Associate Professor H. T. Abbott (Washington State University), E. B. Stiefwater (Milwaukee County Extension Service), Ralph R. Clark (Oregon State College), and R. B. Farnham (The Horticultural Society of New York, Inc.)

# PART I

## Chapter I

# *INTRODUCTION*

This book is addressed to beginners. When I began to write it, I sent a questionnaire to landscape design chairmen of the National Council of State Garden Clubs, asking what kind of information was most sought by home gardeners.

Many replied that garden literature was too general. Some said the questionnaire was too general. And I have responded by writing what will probably be criticized as a general book.

I have long observed that many beginners want to plan a garden backwards. They are concerned about a final detail and impatient about groundwork. They do not see that the effectiveness of the detail depends on the groundwork. It is this same desire to put the detail first and refuse to look at the overall picture that produces disappointment when plant information fails to provide a precise answer to each individual question.

In the first place, it cannot. And in the second place, the nearest thing to comprehensive specific information can only be provided in garden encyclopedias and books on specialized subjects. Many excellent ones are available.

The difficulty here is that inexperienced gardeners don't know what to look for, and the sources that could help them remain largely untapped. A second problem is that isolated facts are often of no help at all unless they are related to a broader pattern, a larger framework of reference.

The purpose of this book is to provide such a framework in very simple terms; to try to establish a meaningful base from which to think about garden design and the use of plants to express a design. Most gardeners have more good ideas of their own than they ever allow themselves to use; often it simply does not occur to them to take outdoors to the yard the sort of curiosity and creative effort they bring to problems inside the house.

9

It is my hope that I can help them a little to realize the opportunities the smallest bit of land presents; to appreciate that some part of man's enormous imaginative resources resides in every individual; and to enjoy their gardens.

❀ ❀ ❀

The smallest garden illustrated in this book (Figure 48) is 12 feet wide and 44 feet long. The largest property (Figures 45 and 46) is a pie-shaped lot 132 feet long, 100 feet wide at one end and 35 feet wide at the other. Of this area about one-fourth is occupied by a house, a drive, and a detached garage, so that the actual garden is considerably smaller. In general this book is addressed to readers with properties up to 100 by 75 feet, of which, naturally, the garden is a smaller part.

## Chapter II

# BACKGROUND

A garden of several acres is an independent unit in which the planner wrestles only with natural physical conditions, but small gardens in closely populated areas are controlled every bit as much by their man-made environment as by climate and soil and topography. They cannot be considered in a vacuum, or designed as though the edges of the drafting board were the limits of the horizon.

To write a short book about small garden design in this rapidly changing age is, therefore, difficult and even presumptuous. On the other hand, the very difficulty is a challenge to stress the infinite variety that garden-making offers the owner of a small property, and to convey some feeling of its excitement against the varied background of America.

## The Development House

There is the situation of the owner moving into a raw new housing development where the entire acreage has been stripped for building. The houses, split level, ranch style, and modern colonial, look from the front windows across a treeless street to bare front yards, and from the rear windows to a plot of land adjoining the plots of three neighbors. Ten, twenty years hence, the community will have a garden style of its own, and it is the owners who are now laying down lawns, and planting trees and shrubs and flowers, who will have created that style. What a chance awaits them, while planning individually, to look ahead and visualize the total picture. How important it is to choose trees thoughtfully, to appreciate the value of quick-growing screen material, to plan the backyards intelligently so that neighborly harmony is promoted rather than disrupted.

## The Old House

At another extreme, there is the owner who has moved into one of the dated pockets common in older residential areas. The style of building repeats itself, and he finds the architectural background is Victorian Gothic, imitation Tudor, Greek Revival, early American, or whatever. He cannot escape the style around him, and he is wise if he doesn't flout it too strenuously in his garden. This doesn't mean that he must forgo individuality; far from it. The important thing is to remember that certain types of garden belong to certain types of setting, and to attempt to reproduce a magazine picture of a beautiful garden belonging to another kind of setting can lead only to disappointment. Obvious as this sounds, it is extraordinary how many people do ignore an environment pressing on their boundaries.

The existence of individual communities of houses, all more or less of a kind, is part of the fascination of America, and it should be part of a gardener's inspiration. The story of how they came about is a bit of local history, with ramifications often into politics, economics, the fashion of a period, the idiosyncrasy of a builder, the nature of local building materials, the skill of a mason or craftsman who has set his inimitable stamp on walls and doorways, and so on. Sometimes the style is dictated by climate and topography, and sometimes it is evidence of an influx of settlers with a common European or New England or Southern background, or a common cultural interest or religious purpose.

But whatever the story, forgotten or remembered, the gardens of America are inseparable from a background as varied as the people who live in them and the forces of nature and man that beat upon them. Perhaps fog rolls in from the ocean at morning and night; or there is salt in sea-borne breezes; or the town lies under the shadow of a mountain; or dust blows in from a desert; or there are bitter winds in winter and intolerable heat in summer.

These are the factors that largely determine the character of the garden. They are a facet of reality naturally beyond the scope of the nursery catalog photographer, who must portray plants grown under ideal conditions, and in so doing convey a sense of uniformity that would make gardening as dull as ditchwater. To the plant lover the variability of plants is a mainspring of interest; the garden artist seeks often not for a perfectly formed tree or shrub, but for one with individuality of shape, some curiousness, even some grotesqueness, that makes it ideal for his purpose. The memorable quality of many a garden derives from an old tree seared and twisted by storm. The Chinese, who have developed a highly sophisticated garden art, deliberately introduce features calculated to produce awe, so that the viewer's perception will be sharpened and he will not be lulled by a plethora of prettiness.

## The Small City Garden

The dweller in a great city is even more the servant of his immediate environment than the suburban or small town resident. His surroundings are constantly threatened by change, and, in a city like New York, which looks permanently more blitzed than London did a short ten years after World War II, and where one is oppressed sometimes by the thought that a mad cook is at work, who has lost his recipe but goes on adding ingredients and beating the mix in the hope that something will come of it, the effects can be downright devastating. Cliffs of concrete arise to imprison the yard, a newborn factory spews noxious fumes over the neighborhood, the street is widened and half a garden plot falls to the bulldozer. Every big city experiences to a greater or lesser degree the waves of change that convert a residential neighborhood into an industrial or commercial area; that the transition is often arbitrary and needlessly ruthless is a tragedy that better planning and a more enlightened approach will, it is hoped, in time avert or at least alleviate.

It is out of this contrived turmoil, this seemingly endless and often senseless destruction, that city gardens are born and, by some miracle, not only persist, but acquire their own peculiar charm. City people are often a restless lot; they tend to move more often than suburban folk and their gardens bear evidence of this ebb and flow of ownership. Projects are begun and not finished, or finished by other hands, and the garden becomes a patchwork of summers, a sort of biographical glimpse of a procession of occupants; in old parts of an old city, a museum, sometimes, of ghosts.

And overshadowing all this ant-like, day-to-day, season-to-season activity, is the enduring character of the city itself, rooted no less in its geographical position and its age than in the story of its founders, their approach, haphazard or methodical, to street planning, their taste in building, and the structural materials upon which they drew.

Boston, for example, built largely of brick in the early days, used brick extensively in paving. Much of the old paving still exists and imparts a distinctive and cherished quality to certain parts of the city. In New York, heavy bluestone flags, brought in huge quantities from the Catskills in the nineteenth century to pave sidewalks and delineate a standard rectangular path in the gardens of brownstones and old brick houses, have frustrated decades of gardeners as much as they have delighted those with the muscle and the will to make of them the good use they deserve. In New Orleans, French and Spanish influence was responsible for the indestructible charm of enclosed courtyards, intricate ironwork and beautiful doorways.

In San Francisco, steep ascents and the dazzling waters of the Bay are as much a part of the picture as the gardens themselves. The flat symmetry of the Midwest; the mixture in Miami of fabulous modern luxury and old, solid, middle-class permanence; the rolling boulevards and sense of boundless horizons of Los Angeles: it is impossible to isolate the gardens from these varying backdrops. True, the gardener, absorbed in his own little lot, will not pay much attention to them; but they are there nonetheless and their presence must be recognized; gardens canot be rolled out with the uniformity of nursery catalog photographs.

**Chapter III**

# *PLANNING*

A new gardener is often so anxious to get in his first petunia and see his first bulbs ablooming that he won't wait to plan his yard, let alone do basic construction work. Then a friend gives him some plants and he sees a flowering shrub at a nursery that he simply must have. The next thing is a medley of plants doing pretty well and it seems a pity to disturb them. The garden is never really made, and over the years the labor that goes into trying to make something look right that never can be right is far greater than that required for a first big effort.

## The Structural Foundation

Plants are not furniture, to be moved about at will; digging them up is not only laborious but usually sets them back, and in locations where growing conditions are difficult, to move them from a place where they are happy, or are making a slow but sure adjustment, may be fatal. The hit-or-miss gardener is therefore constantly faced with the alternatives of irritation from a plant that is out of balance, or the exertion and hazards of moving it. From the design point of view it is better to lose it, but there are surely enough unavoidable demands on one's time and energy without creating occasions for double and triple effort.

Poor placing of a wall or major structure is even more disastrous than bad planting, because it is often impossible to correct without great expense and literally tearing up parts of the garden.

A garden with a good foundation requires a minimum of maintenance and can sustain periods of real neglect. If replacements have to be made, the project is a simple one of substituting plants of comparable size and type.

Planning a garden does not mean that everything has to be

done at once; it does mean that what is done fits into an over-all scheme that has been previously determined. If grading or construction work is required, it is most desirable that this be done before a single plant goes in, if for no other reason than to avoid damage by workmen handling building material and equipment.

There are times, of course, when paving or a wall has to be deferred because of expense; when this is so any planting should be done well away from the area affected, or should be strictly temporary in character.

After the plan has been made, and walls, paths and steps either finished or staked out, the first things to be planted are the big ones, such as trees and major shrubs, then the lawn, if there is to be one. Not only does an unseeded lawn area create dust, but the lawn is such a permanent and conspicuous feature that the sooner it is started the better. The trees and large shrubs establish the skeleton of the planting, and from there one moves toward the detailed effects. Many people want to work in reverse.

## The Approach

On the small lot, hemmed in by other small lots, the first consideration is a convenient arrangement of essential areas, such as a place to sit outdoors in reasonable privacy, a place to dry the clothes, a place for the children to play, and space for planting. The means of getting from one part of the garden to another must also be worked out, and, if there is a garage, the walk from the drive to the front door is of very great importance.

Planning a garden involves also thinking about the kind of garden you want, and the practical problems you will have to meet. Some people like to review the situation in detail before they allow themselves to think of a design. Others take a quick look and are fired with an idea. When the idea is an exciting one, it may provide an impetus that is lacking when the approach is more methodical, and actually make it easier to contend with factors that cannot be ignored. It is amazing what a different complexion an obstacle will assume if it is viewed not just as an obstacle but as a challenging element in a design.

Considerations affecting a garden plan include:

1. The architecture of the house.
2. The nature of adjacent structures.
3. The amount of sunlight and where it falls longest.
4. The position of an existing tree or trees.
5. Whether the soil is deep and easily worked, or shallow and stony.
6. Air pollution (important in the city).
7. Prevailing winds.
8. A neighboring incinerator.
9. The location of garbage cans.
10. The family pet and straying pets.

Sometimes all the factors that will affect the garden are not apparent at first glance in a new home. It is therefore wise to take a little time to learn what they are.

## The Style of the Garden

Very often a new gardener has never thought about whether there is one kind of garden that he likes more than another, but if he ponders a little he will usually discover that he does have a preference.

Making a garden, no matter how simple, is a creative endeavor, and it should relate to the person who owns it and be in some way a conscious expression of himself. A good professional is at pains to find out the kind of garden in which his client will be most happy; he knows that it will, in time, take on something of the character of the person who cares for it, and that the feeling of the garden is most likely to be preserved if the owner is at home in it and can take delight in maintaining it. Every garden is a chore sometimes, but no real garden is nothing but a chore.

There are many kinds of gardens. The broad categories of formal and informal represent the crudest kind of classification. Rather than thinking within this framework, it is better far to ask yourself first what gardens you have most admired and would most like to live with. Never mind if your thoughts leap to a garden more complicated than anything your plot will permit; this is only the first step in the evolution of an idea.

Maybe your feeling will be linked to something as intangible as a pattern of light and shade; or to an old wall; or to a garden you knew in childhood; or to a garden that enchanted you in a book; or to a painting; or to bright colors or just greenness; or, even, to a particular plant; but whatever it is, let that feeling be the *imaginative* springboard for your effort. The rules for garden design can be learned; and a garden can obey all of them and be utterly dull. Imagination provides the individual quality that arrests the beholder and gives real joy to the garden's creator. It is the most difficult aspect of gardening to explain, and one of the most important.

It goes without saying that your dream may be curtailed by common sense. No matter what your secret yearnings, for instance, it is unwise to embark on a project for which you are temperamentally or economically unsuited. Some kinds of garden demand a lot more work than others, and if you are irked by little fussy jobs or repetitive labor, choose a garden that calls for trees or large shrubs and plenty of rich, self-sustaining ground covers. In construction, use materials that don't require painting or other upkeep, and for accents use a garden feature, such as a piece of sculpture or pottery, rather than specimen shrubs or clumps of bright flowers.

If, on the other hand, you love to putter, and are more interested in minute variations than in big effects, make a rock garden or a herb garden or a specific kind of flower garden. If you yearn for the spoils of the harvest and consider flowers a frivolity, plant fruit trees, berry-bearing bushes, herbs and vegetables. Some of the loveliest trees are fruit trees. Many kitchen-garden plants are decorative and can be worked into a general planting: parsley, for example, is a delightful edging plant; strawberries make a splendid ground cover; a number of herbs are pretty border subjects; the Jerusalem artichoke looks like—in fact, is—a sunflower.

There are those for whom a garden identified with a period in history, such as Colonial times or Shakespeare's England, may have a special appeal; such a garden affords scope for scholarly research as well as for horticultural skill. Many old houses lend themselves very well to this kind of garden.

Size is not a limiting factor in choosing a *type* of garden. The Japanese have been centuries in perfecting the development of gardens in minute areas, and there can be no better preparation for organizing a very small area with simplicity and taste than a study of Japanese landscape design. Any style of garden can be beautiful; the important thing is not to let yourself be persuaded to make the kind of garden you don't want.

## Design Suggestions

The rules for garden design are the same as the rules for any art form: a main focus of interest around which the design is built, secondary focal points or accents, integration (unity), rhythm, balance, harmony. Students of flower arrangement are sensitive to these principles; obedience to them is implicit in a good garden. In a sense, a garden is never finished, and it usually takes several years to bring it to a point where every small part is a balanced and pleasing element of the whole. The broad picture, the general scheme, however, should be apparent from the beginning, and this is why a plan on paper, or expressed in a three-dimensional model, is so important. There are people who can look at a piece of land and visualize proportions so accurately that they can see the completed picture without translating their ideas into any other medium; but they are rare. For nearly everyone distances on the ground are deceptive. For them the only way to test an idea is to express it on a drafting board.

The following general principles and suggestions should be borne in mind when making a plan:

1. A long narrow strip of land can be made to seem shorter by breaking it into smaller areas or by introducing different levels.

2. A small property can be made to look larger by running a diagonal axis from one corner to another.

3. The garden should be planned with the thought in mind of how it will look as you approach the house from the street and how it will look from inside the house.

4. The width of paths should be in scale with the property, but no major path should be less than three feet wide. The

front path if possible should not be less than four feet wide.

Owners of small lots sometimes feel that they must introduce curves in the manner of those they have seen on a large estate. This is likely to result in a tortuous path that is neither beautiful to look at nor comfortable to walk upon. If there is a curve, it should be a very simple one.

5. Plants, walls and features should be in scale; that is, they should bear a pleasing relationship to each other, to the house, and to the dimensions of the area. There are times when deliberate distortion is practiced to get a desired effect; but the distortion should be a planned one and not an unfortunate mistake. There is an important difference.

6. Tall thin planting will emphasize the narrowness of a long narrow property. Similarly, a square piece of land will look more square if the planting is all low and rounded. Uniformity of height produces monotony in any garden. Trees bring the sky into the garden.

7. In a small rectangular area, a formal arrangement of paths and planting is often the easiest and most satisfactory. A formal plan need not be stiff; if you want to play down the formal aspect, planting can be asymmetrical and plants with a loose, informal growth can be chosen. And if you do not have an inbuilt resistance to symmetry, a tiny formal garden of low-growing plants enclosed by walls of shrubbery can be charming. Formal geometric gardens are often identified in the popular mind with the beds of begonias and coleus common in public parks, in the middle of a vast expanse of lawn. The same kind of design in an intimate setting in a city garden can have a totally different effect. In a very small space, an informal garden often looks merely untidy. It is also an invitation to overplanting, the bane of small properties.

### Making a Plan

The whole idea of a plan is alarming to some, but the technique need not be complicated, especially on properties of the size discussed here. One way is to draw it on paper; another is to make a simple model. The advantage of a model is that it shows vertical objects in the third dimension; it is not always easy to visualize these on a flat drawing.

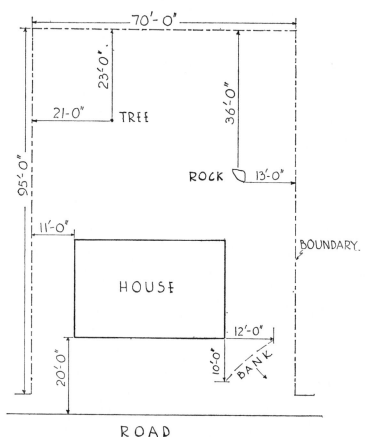

R O A D

Fig. 1.   Measuring the lot.

Whichever method is chosen, the first step is to measure the lot and decide on a scale.

Measuring may be done with a 25-ft., 50-ft., or 100-ft. tape. One person alone can do the measuring, by anchoring one end of the tape with a stone, or a peg driven through the loop at the end of the tape, but it is much quicker and easier if two people work together.

The scale is the number of feet represented on the plan by an inch. For instance, the plan of a piece of land measuring 30 ft. x 50 ft. will measure 7½ in. x 12½ in. if drawn at a scale of ¼ inch to a foot. The scale to choose depends on the size of the property; the smaller the property, the larger the scale. A scale of ¼ to ½ inch to a foot is usually a convenient one for a small garden.

1. ON PAPER. The plan may be made on ruled graph paper (cross-section paper), or on plain paper using an architect's scale. An architect's scale is simply a special kind of ruler, marked in such a way that it is easy to use fractions of an inch to represent a foot. It can be bought at any art supply store.

It is often easier to see big relationships in a design at a very small scale. After a preliminary, small-scale sketch, the plan can be worked out carefully at a larger scale.

Measuring for a new garden, where there is no planting, is very simple. Mark all measurements as you take them on a rough freehand plan. Locate the house on the lot, as shown in the diagram (Figure 1). Locate doors, windows, porch, etc. If there is an outcrop of rock or a tree or other permanent object on the property, locate its position by measuring from two lines, such as boundary lines, at right angles to each other. If there is a sharp drop in level, show where this occurs. Make a note of features outside the property line that will affect the plan. Show the direction of north and south.

When you have all the data you need, draw the plan carefully to scale. Work out the design on tracing paper placed over the plan. Be prepared to make several drawings before you are satisfied. When you have found the design you want, transfer it to the scaled plan.

2. WITH A MODEL. To make a simple model, choose as large a scale as the size of the property permits. Cut a piece of cardboard or bristol board to the correct dimensions of the lot, and glue it to a board large enough to allow space all round the cardboard. A piece of thin plywood or masonite makes a suitable board. Locate the house by drawing it in thick pencil.

To represent paving and all walk areas, get gray or tan paper. Get green paper for the planting areas, and have a piece of blue paper on hand for a possible pool. For structural features, little wooden blocks or the bits of lumber discarded in a carpenter's shop are suitable. You may want to use the simplest material and merely indicate positions; or you may find yourself enjoying the project so much that you want to go to quite a lot of trouble to devise fairly realistic symbols.

For trees and shrubs, the medium may be a simple material like modeling clay or wood, or it may be colored sponge attached to sticks, dried weeds such as goldenrod, or fragments of artificial greenery and flowers from a millinery store. The landscape design exhibitors who make models for flower shows go to a great deal of trouble to simulate the objects depicted.

Having attached the "lot" to the board and assembled the other materials, the next thing is to indicate existing trees and structures, and to show features of the property that are important to the scheme of the garden. These may be the wall of an adjoining house, or a structure or tree in a nearby property that you want to shut out or bring into your design. You have now done with the existing situation and are ready for your own creative effort.

## Living and Utility Areas

In choosing the living area, you will want to consider privacy, shelter from sun and wind, convenience to the house, and outlook. Consideration of shade will be tied to the time of day the area is most in use. And don't forget the sky; in cities this can be a precious commodity. If there is an opening between buildings where the sunset can be seen as a panel, try not to arrange the living area so that you turn your back on it. You may even want to frame your panel of sky with planting.

If you are using the model technique, cut out a piece of the gray or tan paper to represent the living area and drop it in place, but don't fasten it with glue. You may like to estimate the size of the area with your eye and scale it afterwards, or you may like to decide on the size first and cut the paper to scale. Locate the drying area in the same way, and the children's play area. Locate the front walk.

This disposes of basic utility areas, and, with certain reservations, the rest of the garden should be adjusted to them, and not vice versa. The result of this priority of attention is not, as might at first appear, to make them dominant features of the plan, but rather, by alloting them functional positions, to prevent their intrusion into the picture you want to create.

## The Planting Area

You may now proceed with the planning of the remaining space. Cut out pieces of green paper (planted areas) and gray or tan paper (walks) and try them on the cardboard lot. You will have to do a lot of snipping and changing, but when you have a basic design that pleases you and relates satisfactorily to the living area, paste all the pieces on the cardboard; or, if you prefer, identify the different areas with paint or colored crayons. Next, put trees and shrubs in position. At this stage, try to think of plants as shapes and heights.

You probably won't want to go any farther than this with your model; you will have established the main outlines of your garden and the position of major objects, and these will not be affected by detail work.

The next thing is to estimate the dimensions of the areas you have laid out by measuring them on the model or the plan. If they seem unreasonable, work at the design some more. When the design and the measurements please you, mark the measurements on the plan or the model.

### From the Plan to the Ground

You now have a "blueprint" of your garden, ready for translation on the ground. This is done by staking out the different areas. You will need only a measuring tape and plenty of cord and pointed stakes. Locate every position on the ground by measuring from two base lines at right angles to each other, as explained above.

### Grading

When the plan calls for changes in the existing level, the grading required is the next step in making the garden. Grading is essentially modeling the surface of the lot for convenience and beauty. Many crimes are committed in its name.

Good grading is an important part of garden planning. Generally speaking, the natural contours, the natural flow of the land, should be preserved as much as possible; quite apart from the appearance, it is easier to adjust the garden to the contours than the contours to the garden. Certain adjustments may have to be made, to permit drainage, to ease a steep slope, to make steps and walks and flower beds; but these are very different from slicing off every little hummock and rise. Unfor-

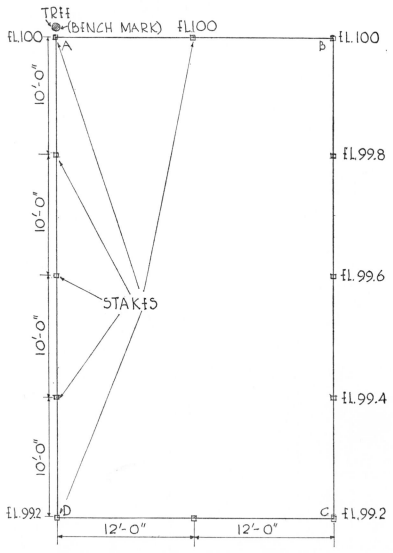

Fig. 2. Diagram showing grading method in plan.

tunately, many people do not come into possession of their land until after a bulldozer has done its brutal work.

When a part of the garden has to be graded, strip the topsoil to a depth of six to eight inches, or more, before making adjustments in level. The topsoil is the valuable growing earth of the garden; do not bury it, but pile it up to one side until grading is finished, and then spread it evenly.

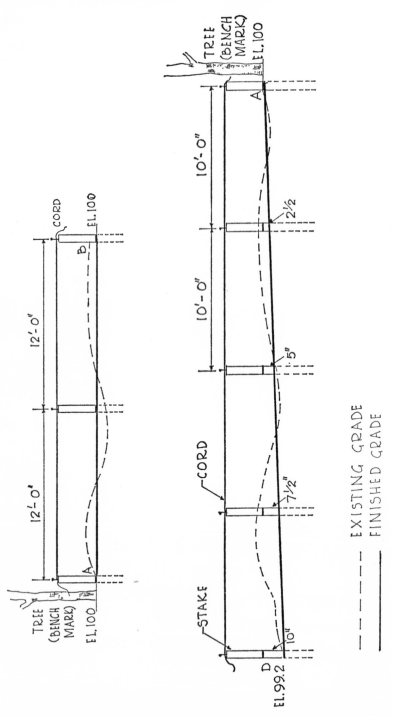

Fig. 3. Diagrams showing grading method in section. The pitch is one-quarter of an inch in a foot.

On a big job, grades are located with surveying instruments. It is possible, however, to do simple grading on a small home property with pointed stakes, a length of mason's twine, and a line level. A line level can be bought at a hardware store; mine cost sixty-eight cents. It is hooked onto the cord and when the bubble is on dead center in the glass the line is level.

Have enough stakes to stake the area to be graded at 10-foot intervals. Mark each stake with black paint or a heavy pencil six inches from the top. Start from a point where the grade is right, and drive the first stake into the ground until the black mark is flush with the ground. Drive a nail into the top of the stake and tie the cord to it.

Drive the rest of the stakes into the ground at 10-foot intervals, in line with the first stake. When you come to the end of the line of stakes, stretch the cord over the top. If you are working alone, secure the cord to a nail driven into the top of the last stake. Using the line level, adjust the height of each stake until the line is level. If you are grading for level ground and not for a slope, the line of black marks on the stakes represents the level of the finished grade.

If you want to slope the ground, make a second mark the correct distance below the first mark on each stake. The second line of marks represents the finished grade. It is a good idea to use a different color for the finished-grade marks.

Figures 2 and 3 explain the method diagrammatically.

Actually, an area should never be absolutely level; a slight pitch is required for drainage. The minimum pitch for unpaved ground is one-quarter of an inch in a foot, and for a paved area one-eighth of an inch in a foot.

## After Grading

When grading is completed, proceed with laying out the garden.

To define a curve for a bed, lay a hose on the ground and keep moving it until the line is satisfactory. Beware of a line that is full of little scallops, which will look jumpy and fussy in the completed garden; keep the curve simple.

To make a circle, locate the center by measuring from the center of the circle on the plan to fixed points at right angles to each other, such as a window of the house, or a tree, or a stake on the boundary. Measure the radius and cut a piece of cord of the same length, with a little to spare. Tie one end to a stake and drive the stake into the ground at the center of the circle. Wind the cord around a second stake until the unwound length corresponds to the length of the radius. Holding the free stake in the hand, describe the circle on the ground with the point of the stake.

Don't be dismayed if the proportions on the ground look different from the plan; an unplanted bed tends to look larger than one that is full of shrubs or flowers. If the proportions are good on the plan, they will be good in the completed garden. This is the object of making a plan; the eyes can take in the picture at a small scale as it cannot do on the ground. If you are in serious doubt, re-check the measurements.

In a big job it would be unwise to start working on the ground until every construction detail had been solved. This book, however, is concerned with very small properties, and staking out the main areas and seeing them on the ground will make it easier to visualize the next step.

Detail cannot save a bad plan, but it can wreck a good one, and it is the detail, whether it be of construction or plants, that will probably first strike the eye of the beholder. When the time comes it should be worked out most carefully, either on paper, or with a large scale model, or by trial and error. The point is that, with a plan in hand, it can be changed or corrected without upsetting the main scheme.

The good basic work of planning a garden is rather like the foundation of a house; when the house is built you don't think about it, but you would be horribly aware of it if it were shaky or crooked. This is perhaps why so many beginners want to work backwards; when they have looked at gardens they have always reacted perfectly normally and been attracted by a striking detail; they have not thought about the careful preparation that made it possible for that detail to be right. And it is the finishing detail with which you will probably have the most fun and that will give you the greatest feeling of having accomplished something. Let it be the prize at the end of the hard row of digging, literally and figuratively, the foundation.

## Chapter IV

# REMODELING AN OLD GARDEN

The suggestions for making a plan given in Chapter III implied the building of a new garden on a bare or almost bare piece of land. The made garden that comes with the purchase of an old house, and the garden that has become unsatisfactory to its owner, require a different approach.

One often hears someone who has just bought a home say, "There are good things in the garden, but it's terribly overgrown" . . . or, "The garden's inconvenient; there's nowhere to sit outdoors" . . . or, "The house is just what we want, but I don't like the garden."

The problem will be highly individual, but two pieces of advice, contradictory at first glance, are almost always in order: "Don't become so involved with indoor alterations that the garden is postponed indefinitely;" and "Don't be in a hurry."

With regard to the first piece of advice, even if you are not especially garden-minded, the garden is an extension of the house; if it is attractive and usable, family life tends to drift outdoors, reducing wear and tear in the living room, and wear and tear of everyone's nerves, so that for purely practical reasons it is wise to organize the outdoor area.

The urgency of the second piece of advice will depend a good deal on the personality of the new owner. At one extreme, the neat housekeeper, burning to have everything tidy, will tend to make a drastic clearance, only to discover too late that plants have been destroyed that cannot be replaced without years of growing or considerable expense.

On the other hand, the individual to whom it is real agony to destroy a productive thing, will try to keep so many unsuitable or superfluous plants that he will spend his gardening years going out of his way to get from one important area of the garden to another; or looking at something that blocks his view or that he doesn't really like; or stooping to get round a branch that he can't bear to cut.

Somewhere between the two poles of sweeping the board clean and ultra-conservation is the happy medium of discarding what is useless and preserving what is valuable in a new design. To achieve this sometimes places a severe strain on the temperament of the gardener; indeed, it is interesting to note how often surrender to a personal quirk will mar the handwork of someone with ability and taste.

I recall vividly a garden made by a talented amateur. It was a large and beautiful garden, containing a number of units, each with its own particular interest, but it had one serious defect: the entrance to every separate part was so difficult, either because of an excessively narrow walk or an obstructive tree or a malfunctioning gate, that one could not move about the garden without irritation. This is the kind of blemish that the advice of a professional can prevent; he may have just as many personal foibles as the owner, but he will usually have had them schooled out of him so far as his work goes.

The man who is dissatisfied with his old garden differs only from a new owner in that he is more familiar with his problem. He may, however, be just as vague about a solution as the recent purchaser, and for this reason both a new owner and an old one are advised to survey their respective situations on a drawing board.

## The Plan

The technique is the same as that described in the preceding chapter: either draw the lot to scale on a piece of paper, or cut a piece of bristol board corresponding to the size and shape of the property. Show the position of the house, and mark important doors and windows. Then indicate the existing layout of walks, steps and beds, the position of pronounced changes in level, and the location of trees and shrubs.

For the survey of an old garden, it is easiest to work with paper and pencil, since it is simpler and quicker to locate objects with pencil dots than with a lump of clay or a block of wood. Fasten the paper to a board with masking tape and carry it outdoors. If it is not convenient to scale each distance as you go along, simply write in the number of feet. Name the various objects, and if you cannot identify a plant, put a descriptive label.

It will be much quicker if two people can work together, one at each end of the measuring tape. One method is to establish two base lines at right angles to each other and make all measurements from these. The base lines can be projections of two sides of the house, or they can be fence or boundary lines. Another method, which is sometimes practical on a small place and saves a good many steps, it to measure out from a point on the house, such as a window, door, or angle, and to keep moving from object to object. With short distances, the eye is a sufficiently accurate guide as to whether an object is in line. Very important objects can be double-checked.

If the measurements are written in and not scaled on the preliminary drawing, take the board to a table when you have finished measuring and draw the plan to scale. This project may seem a tedious one, but it will give a total view of the layout that cannot be obtained in any other way.

## Study the Existing Pattern

When the survey is complete, study the existing pattern. Even if you have lived with the garden for years, you may be struck by relationships from the design point of view that you had not noticed before. Sometimes an idea is born at this stage, and it is well to have it at the back of your mind when you embark on the next step.

Next, take the plan outdoors and check it against the actual objects, studying each tree or shrub as you do so. It might be a good idea to make two rounds, one a "what I want to keep" trip and the other a "this must go" trip. Use a green pencil to circle plants that without question are to remain in their existing position, a red cross to mark those that are as certainly to be discarded altogether. There will probably be a lot of plants that you are doubtful about; you don't want to throw them away, but you are not certain whether or not they will have to be moved. You may like to put a question mark with a blue pencil against these, or just to leave them unmarked for the time being.

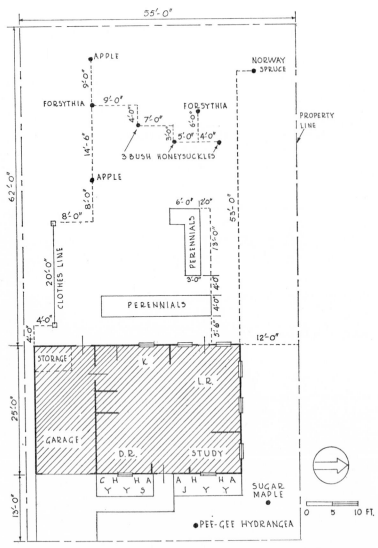

Fig. 4. Plan of old garden. Arrows and conventional dimension lines have been omitted in order not to clutter the plan.

A-Arborvitae          C-Chamaecyparis          H-Hemlock
J-Juniper             S-Spruce                 Y-Yew

*Photograph by Gottscho-Schleisner, Inc.*

Plate 1.   An elegant entrance to an elegant house. Note the change
in paving pattern to define the steps. Evergreens give year-round
interest to the planting; there is room for pockets of bulbs to flower
with the azaleas in spring. Ivy trained on a support and kept
trimmed makes an interesting pattern on the wall at right. Summer-long color could be obtained with pots of an annual such as
petunias in the vases.

*Robert Zion and Harold Breen, Site Planners and Landscape Architects, New York, N. Y.; photograph by Hedrick-Blessing; reproduced by permission of McCall's*

Plate 2.   The entrance to a "standard" house in Cleveland, Ohio before remodeling.

Plate 3, opposite:   Transformation begins with removal of the heavy, light-excluding porch down to its masonry foundation. New steps and a deck over the original foundation lead to the front door. The rest of the porch area between the foundation and the house is filled with flowers. A curved slat screen in front of the big window facing the street gives complete privacy while admitting light from above. A flowering tree, ground cover *(Vinca minor)*, and bulbs replace the lawn between the house and the street.

*Photograph by Gottscho-Schleisner, Inc.*

Plate 4.  The fine old apple tree compelling attention in the center of the lawn is a piece of living sculpture. The simple lines of the flower borders strengthen its effect; fussy beds would weaken it. The proportion of the border along the fence to the size of the area is all-important; if its width were reduced to a mere string the garden would lose much of its character. The fence would be a fine backing for tall perennials. Against the house, a few graceful shrubs are decorative without excluding light and air.

Some agonizing decisions will probably be involved before the new design is complete, but when the question concerns a handsome, well-grown tree that cannot be moved, don't decide to cut it down, no matter how ill-placed it is, until you have stretched your ingenuity to the utmost to build it into the picture you want to create. Sometimes the solution is to reshape the tree by judicious pruning. Plate 4, following page 32, Plates 16, 17 and 18, following page 128, and Plates 25 and 26, following page 192, all show gardens in which the design has been built around, and derives much of its character from, an existing large tree.

An important reason for checking the contents of an old garden before you make your plan is that if you dream up a design that enchants you and then find that a fine tree or shrub interferes with it, it will be harder to make a different design, because you will be thinking regretfully about the one you must discard.

When the plan has been checked against the garden and the plants marked according to whether they are to be kept, moved, or thrown out altogether, put a piece of tracing paper over the plan and re-draw it, putting in only features that are without question to remain in their existing positions. This may or may not include walks, steps and walls.

At this point you may like to make the kind of model suggested in Chapter III. The procedure from now on is the same, except that you will be modifying an existing situation rather than creating a virgin design.

With a new property, it will be remembered, the first consideration is to organize the utility areas, and then to adjust the planting to these. In an old garden, of the kind we are discussing, the plants are there, and it may not be practicable to move them. While a certain amount of compromise is usually necessary, a distinction should be drawn between a desperate compromise and a creative compromise. What appears at first to be a hopeless situation may turn out to be the nub of a really exciting solution.

### Example

The series of figures, 4, 5, 6, 7, illustrate the procedure de-

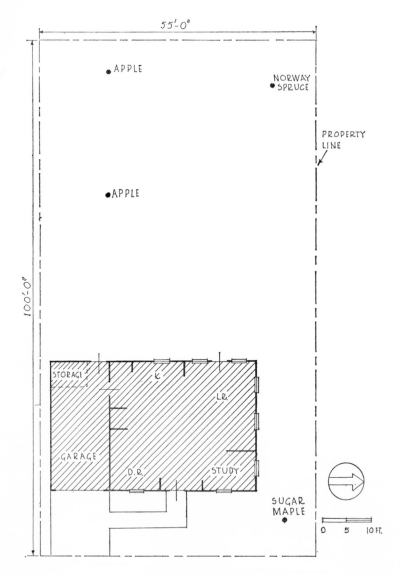

Fig. 5.   Ready for new plan.

scribed above. The marks identifying material to be kept, discarded and moved have been omitted, to avoid confusion, because of the small scale at which the plan is reproduced. The last figure, 7, shows the design of the garden without the distraction of dimensions and labels. Usually, before a satisfactory solution is found, a number of rough sketch plans are made, without reference to careful measurements. The design is then "tested" by drawing it accurately, and the final sketch plan is based on a foundation of detail that has been thoroughly worked out. A rough preliminary sketch plan may look very pretty, but not stand up to careful dimensioning. The home owner may not want to bother with a final sketch plan; it is included here, as it is in professional work, to convey a pictorial idea of the garden. There is no question that, as a dimension plan tests the workability of a rough sketch plan, so does a final, carefully rendered plan show up weaknesses in design.

The garden taken as an example is typical in essence of thousands of small "inherited" gardens and demonstrates several features that occur over and over again—the crowded foundation planting, the placing of shrubs and flower beds without rhyme or reason, the lack of any outdoor sitting area, and so on. Your situation will be different in detail, but it is more than probable that some of the defects of this old garden will exist and a careful study of the way in which they are corrected should help you to solve your own troubles.

The property could be anywhere in the more northerly sections of the country. The family includes pre-teenage children.

The house is a colonial style two-story residence of mellow, unpainted brick, with white trim. The suggested plan would be equally suitable if the house were of frame, or fieldstone, or stucco, or painted brick, but if it were of any of these, the treatment of walls and paving should be studied in relation to the color and texture of the house. A successful landscape job depends a great deal on the choice of structural materials. While contrast is often desirable, too many kinds of material are irritating and destroy the unity of the picture. It is impossible to lay down hard and fast rules for what to put with which; the chapter on building materials will help to clarify the matter. Try looking at buildings around you and noting combinations that jar or please. Observations you make yourself are far more valuable than arbitrary do's and don'ts.

### The New Garden

1. FOUNDATION PLANTING. The foundation planting poses questions that are almost constants in home landscape work. In

an old garden, the problem can be acute, and it is best to settle it firmly and finally at the outset. A general discussion of foundation plantings is given in Chapter V. In this chapter we are concerned with the disposition, in a specific situation, of a typical foundation forest.

There are three columnar arborvitae and a well-grown moss chamaecyparis against the front of the house. Four hemlocks, no doubt innocent-looking feathery little shrubs when they were planted, are beginning to get out of hand beside the windows. In the fore-planting, there are four nicely shaped, rather spreading Japanese yews, a stiff little blue spruce about two feet high, and a small pointed juniper. The spruce and the juniper were probably put in as replacements, or to add a final touch of chic.

Figures 6 and 7 show how these plants are used in the new garden. The three columnar arborvitae provide a screen on the south side of the patio, both for the laundry yard and for the neighboring house. In addition to giving privacy, they make a handsome evergreen mass to be viewed from the living room and the kitchen window in winter.

One yew is planted at the corner of the house near the garage, and one next to the street by the drive. The other two are planted behind the sugar maple, opposite the northeast corner of the house. The yew is placed behind the maple rather than at the corner of the property next to the street because it is a mistake to conceal the trunk of a fine tree. The old sugar maple, standing just where it is as a sort of solitary guardian, should not be cluttered by a heavy fore-planting; on the other hand, the dark mass of yew behind it, as it increases in size, will help to set off the trunk. If yew were not available from the foundation planting, a mass of mountain laurel would be handsome here.

The hemlocks are moved to the space between the house and the property line, where they screen the living room and study windows from the adjoining property. Hemlocks like shade; the space on the north side of the house is too narrow for general garden use; and most people like to screen the windows of rooms in constant use. Trees grown as a hedge are planted closer together than trees grown as specimens. If the hemlocks were planted on the boundaries of the play area, they would in time

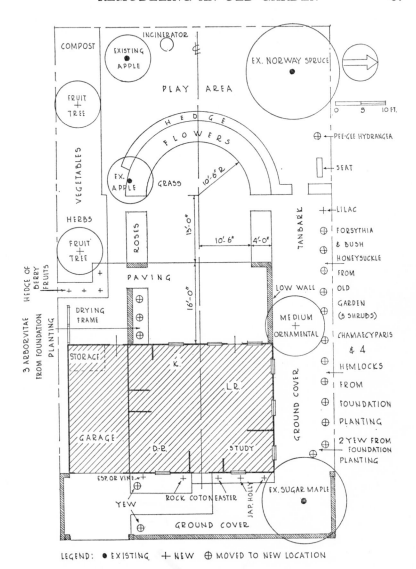

Fig. 6. The new plan, showing major dimensions and location of new and transplanted material.

crowd it, since there are not enough for a hedge here and, with plenty of room, they would make wide growth.

The moss chamaecyparis (*Chamaecyparis pisifera squarrosa*) is planted at the far end of the hemlocks, opposite the northwest corner of the house. It is an individual and beautiful plant, and by putting it here it can be seen from the terrace.

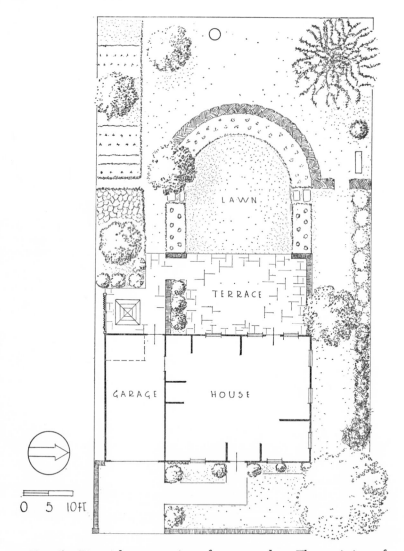

Fig. 7. Pictorial presentation of new garden. The omission of dimensions and labels gives a clearer picture of the design.

The blue spruce and the juniper are rejected. Juniper would not thrive on the north side of the house, and there is no place for the little pointed specimen in the main garden scheme. Nor is there any spot for the two-foot blue spruce; it could conceivably go near the west property line, but apart from the fact that it is not a good aesthetic companion for the Norway spruce, it would be utterly out of scale with it for so long that altogether this is an occasion when the most fanatical conservationist should harden his heart, or search his mind for the friend who is longing for a little blue spruce.

2. THE FRONT YARD.    Treatment of a small front yard is another controversial subject. The one on the plan is thirteen feet deep. A depth of up to twenty feet would look spacious in a city yard, because the fronts of adjoining city houses usually present a continuous façade and the preponderance of high buildings and masses of masonry tend to magnify every little bit of green. In the suburbs, however, there are open thoroughfares, trees, and space between dwellings, and the unenclosed front lot shrinks in consequence. There is a tendency to dot these little areas with posies of annuals, perennials, or small flowering shrubs, and often the result is so spotty that it detracts from the dignity of the approach. It is usually most satisfactory to keep the small front garden very simple, and to study carefully the kind of treatment that will be most in harmony with the architecture of the house.

In the garden under discussion, dwarf to medium box-leaf holly *(Ilex crenata convexa)* is suggested for the two small shrubs to the right of the door. This is a rich evergreen, and it will grow in the shade of the maple. These two plants, with a ground cover, will give a little dressing to this side of the house, which is all that is needed. A quantity of plants here would compete with the maple and clutter the design.

The plant on each side of the door is one of the rock cotoneasters, trained in a low espalier against the wall. This plant has a great deal of character, and the red berries are attractive. If the climate is too severe for cotoneaster, a medium-spreading juniper can be used.

At the corner, next to the garage, the orange-berried firethorn *(Pyracantha coccinea lalandi)* would be handsome espaliered to the wall. It has a northern limit of hardiness roughly below the midwestern states and Massachusetts, except in coastal sections. Beyond this limit, Boston ivy *(Parthenocissus tricuspidata)* would be excellent for this corner. Boston ivy clings tightly to a wall by means of little appendages, and the color of the autumn foliage is wonderful. The self-supporting climbing hydrangea *(Hydrangea petiolaris)* is another possibility. Its foliage is more massive than that of Boston ivy. In a sunny location, its white flowers are handsome. (Neither of these vines is suitable for painted or frame walls; for these, a vine grown on a removable support should be used.)

Baltic ivy, pachysandra, and periwinkle *(Vinca minor)* are all suitable ground covers for the space between the shrubs in the little strips of planting in front of the house. Baltic ivy is smaller-leafed and hardier than English ivy. It is also less luxuriant, and this would be an advantage here. It is to be preferred over the other ground covers mentioned, because it would flatten itself against the base of the wall and send shoots up it. Any tendency of these ground cover plants to become invasive and smother the shrubs could easily be controlled in such a small space.

Grass would be a nagging chore in the remainder of the front garden, and it would not grow under the maple. One answer would be to surface the area with crushed stone or gravel of a color that harmonizes with the house, and to continue with this material in the space between the evergreens and the house on the north side. Weeds could be controlled easily with a weed killer. Another solution would be to plant solidly with an evergreen ground cover. If English ivy were hardy in the area, its heavier growth would make it superior to Baltic ivy. There will be virtually no traffic on the north side of the house, but steppingstones could be placed amongst the ground cover if desired.

### Edging the Front Yard

In suburban and small town gardens, the boundary of the front yard is often left to meet the sidewalk without any edging whatsoever. A curb at least eight inches high undoubtedly adds to the finish of the yard. In the problem under discussion, the drive and walk are light colored concrete, and this material would be suitable for the curb. An alternative, which would give a little more distinction, would be to build a wall of brick similar to that of the house, eight inches thick (the length of a brick) and one foot high, with a flagstone cap, extending of course along the far side of the drive. With the brick of the house thus extended to the sidewalk and picked up on the other side of the drive, the walk to the front door could be of brick and/or flagstone, without giving a feeling of spottiness and unrelated materials. A poured concrete walk to the front door of a brick house does not provide very much finish, though it undoubtedly looks better when the edges are softened by a ground cover than when it is smack up against the surface of a manicured lawn. If concrete is used for a front walk, rectangular blocks look better than a plain walk.

Plate 22, following page 160 shows a very nice treatment of a property line curb adjoining a sidewalk.

## Width of Walk

The original walk to the front door of this house was three feet parallel to the street, changing to four feet in the part in front of the door. Three feet is minimum for even such a short front walk, and it would make a better proportion to widen the narrow part by a foot. The approach to a front door should be generous, and should not force guests to walk in single file, or close together in case a false step sends them heel deep into the soft or muddy earth of adjoining beds.

## Garbage Cans

It will be observed that provision is made on this plan for a compost pit at the end of the vegetable garden, and a movable incinerator in the play area. A container must, however, be provided for the collection of bottles and cans, and for other refuse if a compost pit is not acceptable and a refuse disposal unit in the kitchen sink is forbidden by ordinance. Millions of properties in the United States are scarred by the ubiquitous garbage can. The problem possesses acutely local angles, because of the highly individual approach of different municipalities. In the problem under discussion, a sunken can-holder with a movable cover, next to the garage, is the best solution.

## The Terrace

The terrace is raised about six inches above the level of the garden. The lawn will thicken, and if the terrace is made flush with the ground, or only an inch or two above it, it will soon be below the level of the grass. This will make it difficult to drain.

The purpose of the wall is both aesthetic and practical. If the terrace is raised, without a low parapet, there will be something of a feeling that it is floating in space. The wall ties the terrace to the house. Also, a wall or parapet about twenty inches high is useful to sit on, and provides a resting place for glasses and ash trays. On this plan it makes a convenient ledge next to the laundry yard for clothes pins and so on.

An open-work brick wall, eight inches thick, with a flagstone cap one foot wide, is suggested. The one-foot flagstone cap will provide finish and make a ledge of useful width.

Since the house is of unpainted brick, a terrace paved with cut flagstones, or a combination of brick and grayish flagstone, is suggested. This makes a pleasing contrast in material. The terrace should of course be pitched slightly away from the house, so that water drains off into the garden. The level of the terrace in relation to the level of the door-sill into the living room should be studied, so that there is no awkward transition, and no danger of flooding in heavy rains. Leave small openings in the base of the parapet next to the garden to permit a free flow of water.

## The Laundry Yard

The paving is continued into the laundry yard for a more finished job and for the convenience of the housewife when she is hanging wet clothes. A trellis on the south side of the drying yard is covered with a perennial vine planted on the outside of the trellis. A grape vine would be suitable, or bittersweet. The trellis screens the drying yard from the neighbors.

## Paving Informal Areas

Tanbark is used for the path next to the vegetable garden, the play area, and the area north of the terrace. Tanbark is pleasant to look at, comfortable to walk on in wet weather, and an enemy of weeds. Wood chips would also be suitable. Grass would be troublesome to maintain.

## The Planting

The treatment of the main garden, which may be described as a balanced garden, with a little of everything, should be self-explanatory. It could be changed in accordance with the own-er's taste.

## The Terrace Tree

The ornamental tree at the north end of the terrace is the picture tree of the garden and should be selected thoughtfully. Height, shape, foliage and bark should be considered. It should be fairly high crowned. It should not be a messy tree, with leaves that shed constantly, or berried fruit that will squash on the terrace. Since there are several fruit trees in other parts of the garden, a contrasting type of tree is a better choice. The silk tree *(Albizzia julibrissin rosea)*, and a thornless form of the honey locust *(Gleditsia triacanthos inermis)* would both be suit-able. These trees are described in another section of the book.

## Deciduous Shrubs

The big deciduous shrubs from the old garden are used along the boundary line to make a dense screen on the north side of the terrace. A lilac is added at the far end, chiefly because it is so much in the character of the garden. The pee-gee hydran-gea from the old front garden is used as a specimen between the seat and the Norway spruce. The deciduous shrub planting will give spring color from the lilac and forsythia, and in late summer there will be the red berries of the honeysuckles. The picturesque flowers of the hydrangea will persist long after the first frosts have tinged them with rose.

## The Hedge

The hedge defines the shape of the main garden, screens it from the play area, and provides a rich backing for the flowers. It should be at least four feet high. Hemlock, or an upright variety of yew, would be ideal, but if these plants are too ex-pensive, privet can be used. Certain woody trees, such as the hedge maple *(Acer campestre)*, or beech, planted close together and kept trimmed to hedge height, would also be suitable.

## The Flower Beds

Roses would be pretty near the terrace and would provide season-long color, but if they are unacceptable, the two rose beds could be planted with daylilies *(Hemerocallis)*. These are among the easiest plants to maintain, and, if the right varieties are selected, a long succession of bloom is possible. Daylily catalogs list hundreds of kinds and give their flowering dates. Other suggestions for these two beds are dwarf evergreen azaleas, a collection of lilies, chrysanthemums interplanted with annuals, or simply annuals. Whatever treatment is decided on, the two beds should match.

The far border is backed by the hedge, and perennials from the old garden are used as a foundation, with spring flowering bulbs and annuals interplanted in clumps. A mixed border such as this should be planned, not planted in haphazard fashion. Perennials of strong character, such as peonies, make a good backbone, with the other plants grouped around them.

### Edging the Flower Beds

Grass will invade the flower beds if it is not kept out with a masonry, metal, or plastic edging. Edgings are discussed in several places in the book. See Index.

The plant edging for these beds should be a very dwarf evergreen. The so-called dwarf boxwood *(Buxus sempervirens suffruticosa)* must be clipped to keep it to a height of even six or eight inches. The horticultural variety, *Buxus microphylla compacta,* would be better, but it might be difficult to get. Another very dwarf variety is known as Korean boxwood. If box is not hardy, a dwarf variety of Japanese holly, either *Ilex crenata helleri* or a horticultural form, could be used. For the free-standing beds next to the terrace, the edging should completely surround the beds.

When expensive evergreen plants such as boxwood and Japanese holly cannot be managed all at once, one of the annual edging plants may be substituted, or interplanted with evergreens. Boxwood and Japanese holly are easy to grow from cuttings, so that the edging can be built up gradually. Either of these plants will add greatly to the appearance of the area.

The same plant edging may be continued in front of the far bed, or a less expensive one, such as evergreen candytuft *(Iberis sempervirens),* may be used. A permanent dressy edging is somewhat less important for the far bed, backed as it is by a strong hedge, than for the open beds near the terrace.

## Herbs

Some tall growing herbs, such as angelica, the bushy chamomile, and certain artemisias, would, if planted near the boundary, prevent this part of the garden from falling away visually. Herbs are pretty companions for a rose bed, or, indeed, any flowers. It is always convenient to have them as close to the kitchen as possible.

## Bush Fruits

The berry bushes are planted to make a hedge, defining the drying yard and stopping the eye as one looks from the terrace towards the next door property.

## The Play Area

It is often a good idea to keep part of a garden flexible in the early stages. In this garden, the area at the rear is left undeveloped, to provide as much space as possible for play. Later, the owner may want to extend the vegetable garden, or make a cutting garden, or increase the number of fruit trees, or use the space as a naturalistic picnic area.

## Boundary Treatment

This is discussed in a separate chapter. In this garden, no decision is made. It may be convenient for the children of more than one family to play together in a shared area at the rear of adjoining lots. If this is not the case, or if it is felt that the children might stray too far afield, a fence can be erected.

## Pruning and Transplanting

An old garden often calls for drastic pruning. Begin by cutting out all dead wood; this applies to every kind of plant. After that, discrimination is needed. Remember that when most needle-leaf evergreens are cut back to old wood, they will not put out new growth. Unless it is desired to reshape an evergreen, by checking growth in certain areas, confine pruning to shortening growing shoots.

Deciduous material is different; it will grow from old wood. Sometimes pruning that is not considered good by a professional horticulturist is deliberately practiced by landscape designers to get a desired shape. You will have to use your own judgment a good deal in the treatment of overgrown material in an old garden; so much will depend upon the effect you want to produce. Prune spring-flowering shrubs immediately after flowering, to allow a season's growth for next year's blooms. Prune fall-flowering material in early spring. Always use sharp pruning shears, and make clean slanting cuts between buds. Cut weak shoots harder (farther back) than strong shoots. If you are in doubt about a precious plant, get the advice of a local expert. Always work cautiously at first, survey the effect, and then cut some more.

If you are transplanting, cut all broken or bruised roots cleanly, and shorten ones that are too long for the hole. When crowded evergreens from a foundation planting have to be moved, it is usually wise to pay a nurseryman to do it.

## Tree Stumps

Modern tree-cutting equipment includes special saws which cut below the surface of the ground, and when a tree is to be removed the owner should insist on their use. An old garden, however, often contains a stump projecting a foot or more above ground. There is no easy way to remove such a stump. The so-called stump-removing chemicals are generally considered to be doubtfully effective. The two most reliable techniques are digging and blasting. Blasting is the quickest method; *but it should never be attempted by an amateur.* Furthermore, it is an unnecessarily drastic procedure in the average home garden.

Since wood will not burn without air, a fire over the stump will affect only the surface. Often the most practicable method is to cut the stump flush with the ground and cover it with earth mixed with a water-holding substance such as peat moss low-rooted annuals in the soil and, after every crop, chip away or vermiculite. The moist earth will hasten decay. Grow shal-the rotting wood to increase the soil depth.

## Chapter V

# *FOUNDATION PLANTING*

Foundation planting, in its most extravagant form, produces such horrors of overplanting that it becomes a blot on American landscape planning.

It had its innocent beginnings in a period after the Civil War, when the custom of enclosing properties was abandoned, the front yard was deepened, and many houses were built high on unsightly foundations. People felt a need to dress up their larger and more exposed front gardens, and also to conceal the masonry of the foundation. As time went on, the practice offered a golden opportunity to plant dealers with big stocks of needle-leaf material. Too many, alas, failed to consult their consciences, and sold their customers an assortment of plants that, foundation height at the time of planting, a few years later were young forests shutting out light and pressing against the house in a tight embrace with each other and with the building.

A vicious circle developed, in which evergreen stocks were increased to meet the demand for foundation planting, and sales were pressed to get rid of the stocks. The result was a convention so firmly entrenched that when the architecture of the house actually presented no ugly foundation to conceal, the home owner felt as undressed without a foundation planting as a housewife without draperies on her windows. Fortunately, the practice seems to be less rampant than it was; more nurserymen are trained landscape men, obedient to aesthetic as well as business considerations, and more home owners are thinking for themselves. The purchaser of an old garden, however, may very well find that he has inherited some fifteen to twenty evergreens, ill-assorted as to height, texture, and preference for sun and shade, along the front of his house. The redistribution of such a planting was discussed in Chapter IV.

*The planting around the base of a house should never be considered as separate and apart from the plan of the entire garden.*

It is always difficult to bring a fresh approach to a problem around which a number of fixed ideas have been built. The new gardener is in especial danger, because it is natural for him to accept counsel that has wide support. He is well advised, however, in planning his garden, not to stop dead in his thinking when he comes to the strip of ground close to the front of the house, but to consider it as thoughtfully as any other element in the design.

## Winter Beauty

To begin with, the great value of evergreens is their winter beauty. When the deciduous trees and shrubs are skeletons, and the flower border a memory, the evergreens are richly dark, or lovely under a dusting of snow. One can appreciate their form as one never can in summer. How extraordinary, then, to put them where they are only visible as one approaches the house from outside, and in a position where their shape and individuality are lost in a dense planting against a wall.

## Light and Air

It is possible that, apart from the original reasons for a foundation planting, other half-crystallized ideas have contributed to its popularity. Perhaps there is a vague feeling that, with an open boundary in front, a planting against the house will provide some sort of screen. This is ostrich-head logic, of course, because any planting effective as a screen will exclude light and air from windows. Then again, in very cold and exposed locations, a thick planting close to the house serves to some extent as a warm wrap, and the householder returning home on a bitter night may sometimes think how snug his home looks in a mantle of evergreens.

These suggestions may be roundly rejected as having no validity whatsoever, but perhaps they will stimulate thinking about a widely accepted custom. Let each home owner ask himself, "What beauty or value is there in a typical foundation planting?"

Fig. 8. An example of bad foundation planting.

A-Red cedar
B-Japanese yew
C-Spruce
D-Arborvitae

Figure 8 shows a typical foundation planting. The side of the house is completely bare, so that the silhouette is distorted.

## Ugly Masonry

When there is an ugly foundation to conceal, a viny evergreen, such as wintercreeper or English or Baltic ivy, that will lie flat against the wall, will tie the house to the ground much more effectively than a bulge of green only slightly less rigid than the masonry it is designed to hide or than a series of stiff green spots, of whatever height. An evergreen vine can be prevented, if desired, from climbing high on the wall, but a few random shoots will soften the hard line of the foundation.

An unfortunate effect of many conventional foundation plantings is to emphasize an architectural feature that should be played down. For instance, columnar evergreens at the corners of a tall, narrow house draw the eye up and make the house look taller. The same type of house is made to look top-heavy by a line of strong dwarf material of uniform height crouching at the base. The right kind of tree planted at a little distance from the house will shade it, frame it, and modify harsh lines in a way that no foundation planting can.

The above remarks are not intended to imply that shrubs should never be planted in front of the house. Very often a shrub planting is called for; but it should relate to the rest of the garden plan and not represent an independent formula.

## Chapter VI

# CONSTRUCTION MATERIALS

The materials used for paving walks and terraces, and building steps, walls and fences, are the bones of the garden; in cold climates, where they are largely stripped of softening drapery in winter, they are stark and bare for maybe half the year. Quite apart from their function in delineating the design, they can, if their texture and color are unsuitable, jar the harmony of the picture more disastrously than a blaze of inappropriate color on a flowering plant. The plant will not bloom all season; it is also much easier to move it than to tear up a paving or a wall, and yet it is more common to fret over the color of an azalea than over a poor choice of masonry. The structural materials for a garden should, therefore, be chosen with care.

## Natural and Artificial Materials

Structural materials may be divided into two big classes, natural and artificial. It is not possible to draw a sharp distinction between the two, because some "natural" materials must be processed, and many "artificial" materials contain a proportion of natural ingredients. For the purposes of this nontechnical discussion, however, the first class is taken to include wood, stone, brick (essentially baked clay), certain kinds of tile, and iron.

The second class includes concrete and concrete products, such as concrete grille; types of synthetic brick and paving blocks; plastics; some kinds of mosaic; aluminum grille, and so on. In fact, so many synthetic products are pouring onto the market that it is impossible to keep up with them. Many of the new materials possess great possibilities; many have not yet been tested by time, and it is not known how gracefully they will accept the patina of age.

STONE. In a garden, the changes wrought by exposure are of major importance. Some very durable materials, such as granite and other igneous rocks, and some of the dense, fine-grained sandstones, weather slowly, and the appearance of age in even very old structures is often due more to little patches of lichen and moss adhering to the stone than to any breakdown in the material itself. Soft sandstones erode more quickly. Climate, of course, has much to do with a material's resistance to decay.

It is always interesting to visit an old, once elaborate garden that has been allowed to fall into ruin. Real stone is usually intact, though the disintegration of mortar may have caused walls to collapse.

One of the wonderful things about natural rock is its irregularity of pattern. Who has not loitered by a stone wall or sat on a rocky ledge and idly noted the veins of white in a dark mass, the gleam of mica or pyrites, the perfect face of a crystal, the orange-red stain of iron, or the dull green color of serpentine? When a piece of rock breaks, a whole new pattern may be revealed. This infinity of interest is something that only real rock as opposed to synthetic material can provide, and it is the reason why a little, if possible, should be in every garden. Unfortunately, there is a perverse tendency to cut and dress natural rock to make it look as much like synthetic material as possible. Unless random rectangular blocks of stone (i.e., rectangular blocks of irregular size) are handled very skillfully in making a wall, a result may be produced that is more dishonest, and often less pleasing, than concrete.

WOOD. Wood varies not only in its resistance to decay, but in the appearance it presents as the seasons take their toll. Most unstained woods eventually acquire a bleached look, somewhat like the driftwood found on the beach, but not all kinds weather in the same way or at the same speed. Redwood goes through a brown stage before it reaches a final pearly gray.

Everyone is apparently agreed that bald cypress (*Taxodium distichum*) does not require treatment with a preservative if it is to be in contact with earth. After that, opinion divides. Some maintain that redwood and locust may also be used without treatment; others say that redwood may but not locust, and others again that locust is safe but redwood is not. The agents responsible for the deterioration of wood are bacteria, fungi, and insects. It is obvious that their activity must vary under different conditions. Heartwood is the most decay-resistant part of a tree. A factor in determining the degree to which precautions should be taken is the permanence of the structure. A formula for treating wood that is in contact with soil is:

> Saturate backfill with raw creosote and fuel oil. Paint base of post up to four inches above soil surface with a wood preservative containing copper naphthenate. Place a nonrusting water-shedding cover over oil-saturated soil if planting nearby.

BRICK.   Even bricks, which vary in appearance with the composition of the clay from which they are made, and with the method of making them, do not react in a uniform way to the ravages of time. Bricks have been used for thousands of years, and have been, in different places and at different time, of many shapes and sizes. In the United States a common brick measures about 2 x 4 x 8 inches, and weighs about 4½ pounds, or 118 pounds per cubic foot, but the size of a common brick varies somewhat throughout the country. Some bricks have sharper edges than others. It is therefore advisable to test any pattern against the bricks available to see if it will work. Hard-fired common brick makes a durable paving; the softer grades do not.

Old brick is usually less harsh than new brick, and to be preferred for garden work. In areas where much demolition is being done, it is often cheap and easy to get.

A brick wall protected by a flagstone or concrete cap will not deteriorate as rapidly as one in which the top mortar is entirely exposed, since, without a cap, it is impossible to prevent water from getting into the wall.

It is useful to remember that the type of joint used in mortaring bricks in a wall affects the appearance. The different types of joint, with the names used by bricklayers, are shown in Figure 9. With a rake joint, the mortar is least conspicuous. A flush joint is best for a wall that is to be painted. The other types of joint affect the shadow cast by each brick course.

The color of the mortar is also important. If it is in sharp

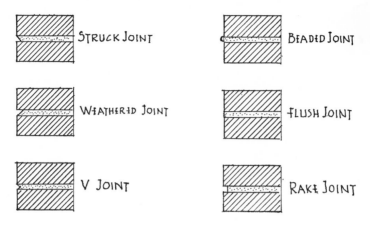

Fig. 9. *Brick joints:* The flush joint should be used for brick that is to be painted. The mortar is least conspicuous with a rake joint. The other types of joint affect the shadow cast by each brick course.

contrast to the color of the brick, the wall lacks an over-all harmony of tone. The color of the mortar should be uniform throughout and not patchy through bad mixing. It is claimed that ready-mix mortars now on the market avoid the mistakes resulting from careless mixing on the job.

TILE. In Mexico and other places where there is a strong Spanish influence, glazed tiles of rich color and elaborate design are used widely and effectively for outdoor paving and garden seats, and as insets in walls. They should be used more in the North, to relieve the monotony of green in shady gardens and to provide color in winter. Some of the imported small mosaic tiles are extremely decorative as a lining for tiny pools. The technique of using them can be learned from craft books and instruction sheets supplied by dealers.

IRON. Magnificent wrought iron work is a heritage of some of the older parts of the country. When available, it can often be worked skillfully into the design of a small garden. It must, of course, be kept painted to prevent deterioration through rust. Iron is very useful for certain types of steps. The shadow cast by it can be important. Iron should, however, be used with discrimination; it can be lost among foliage, and a combination of ornate iron with a flower bed may be altogether too fussy.

## The Gardener and His Materials

The gardener usually feels that he must familiarize himself with a lot of plants. He reads books, studies catalogs, attends botany courses. It is much less common for him to feel that he should learn about rocks and lumber. As often as not, the rounded pebbles and boulders of all sizes that he digs out of a garden in a region where glaciation has deposited material of enormously varied color and composition are treated as just stones to be junked. If he is a craftsman, however, he will see the possibilities of the smaller pebbles for use in a coarse-aggregate concrete paving mix, and of the large boulders for a variety of utilitarian and ornamental purposes.

Similarly, it is the gardener's choice whether he regards the great tree that has died as an obstruction to be hauled away as quickly as possible, or cut up for firewood; or whether he studies it for its value as lumber. It might be larch *(Larix)*, or western red cedar *(Thuja plicata)*, or red cedar *(Juniperus virginiana)*, all excellent woods for outdoor work. It might even be bald cypress *(Taxodium distichum)*, with its fantastic record of endurance under exposure to water and wet earth. It is shocking how often lumber with virtues that make it ideal for a specific purpose is discarded because of the owner's ignorance.

Roughly dressed wood may be combined with stone or used alone for steps; it is an excellent edging for many types of walk. A trunk sawed crosswise provides attractive paving blocks in an informal area. Railway ties make a handsome retaining wall.

## Nature as Inspiration

Students of garden design courses are sometimes advised to go to Nature for inspiration. The expression is vague, embracing as it must a sequoia forest and a patch of fringed gentians, but in the limited reference of rock work it is a most excellent piece of specific advice. Natural ledges and the accidental grouping of stones often present little isolated pictures, pregnant with ideas for the garden. Native stones may even be used as features in a garden, either in informal groups, or placed singly on a rectangular flagstone.

To digress a little, while on this difficult subject of nature as a source of inspiration in garden art, the kernel of the idea may perhaps be illustrated by a literary allusion. Wordsworth, it will be remembered, in his *Preface to Lyrical Ballads*, spoke of "emotion recollected in tranquillity." Poetry is born of emotion, but the raw stuff of feeling cannot be transmitted directly; it must be distilled and subjected to the discipline of art. So, too, beautiful forms in nature should be studied, not with the idea of literal imitation, but so that the picture may sink into the mind and become the wellspring of an art form.

## Indigenous Material

In a country as vast as the United States, different parts of the country are identified with certain types of indigenous stone and certain types of lumber. As likely as not, the soil of the garden will derive from the stone, and living forms of the lumber exist in trees on the property.

The gardener who lives in an area where there are natural resources suited to his needs possesses an advantage over the man who must pick and choose in a market offering a wide number of choices of varied origin. The most authentic, the most honest gardens, are those which are related to the area in which they are made, and it is much easier for the man with natural resources at his command to build a garden that is an organic whole than it is for the man who must do what is virtually catalog shopping. A wide choice of materials, selected away from the site, all too often produces a jarring assortment of colors and textures.

## Every Garden an Individual Problem

Apart from the general principles discussed in the preceding paragraphs, the choice of material, and how to use it, is an individual problem in every garden. Even the method of construction changes in different parts of the country, depending on the depth of the frostline and the condition of the subsoil. Many structural problems must be considered in conjunction with drainage; this again is an individual situation. So long as the gardener is alert to these matters, he can consult books and local experts and guard against mistakes.

## Chapter VII

# *DRAINAGE*

Drainage problems on a small property are more often tied to structural errors of one kind or another than to water-logged soil resulting from sub-surface conditions. Typical difficulties are:

1. A badly-pitched terrace. The terrace should be constructed so that water runs off gently into garden areas away from the house; it should not flow towards the house, or towards one spot close to the house from where it can seep into a cellar. The standard pitch for a terrace is one-eighth to one-quarter inch per foot. On a large terrace, it may be necessary to pitch in more than one direction. If there is a wall or parapet round the terrace, openings (weep holes) should be provided at the base to allow water to escape from the surface.

2. A terrace that cannot drain because it is below the level of adjoining turf.

3. A walk that is too steep, so that water rushes down it and accumulates in a puddle.

4. Steps that have been constructed without a slight wash, or pitch, to enable water to run off; or with a pitch in the wrong direction, so that water runs back towards a riser and forms a puddle.

5. Failure to provide weep holes in a retaining wall. In freezing weather, the accumulated water expands and causes masonry to crack.

6. A raised or flush bed, with an inadequate edging of wood or masonry, so that soil is washed out onto the walk.

7. A roof overhang from which water beats onto plants close to the house, or makes a furrow in the soil.

8. A downspout not connected with an underground drainage system or sewer, causing water to wash out the soil and make a hole below the spout.

9. A poorly graded lawn with areas into which water runs rapidly, forming lakes which drain slowly.

10. Pockets of poor drainage caused by the burial of tightly packed stones and concrete building debris.

11. Water in the cellar, caused by bad grading round the house, or failure, when the water table is high, to provide subsurface drainage.

When a bad condition does exist, sometimes the only satisfactory solution is to tear out the old work, troublesome though this may be. Often, however, a little ingenuity will put things right. Here are a few suggestions:

## Water from a Steep Roof

When it is impossible or difficult to correct the structural defect causing heavy rain to wash off a steep roof onto a bed, damaging plants and eroding the soil, don't plant under the periodic waterfall or heavy drip, but dig a neat trench a few inches deep and a few inches wide pitched gently towards an area where the water can be absorbed. Put pebbles or crushed stone in the trench, flush with the top if the fall is not heavy, and an inch or two below the top if there is danger of the pebbles being washed out. Tamp the stone lightly. Plant in front of the trench if the problem area is close to the wall of the house; the planting will conceal it. If the overhang is considerable, plant behind the trench. If the trench is properly made and filled with graded pebbles of a uniform color, it can be made a decorative border to the bed. Ground covers in the bed can be used to soften it.

## Making a Dry Well

Water from a downspout that cannot be connected with an underground system or sewer can be taken care of by a dry well. A dry well, or swallow hole, is a primitive but still useful method of relieving soil of excess water. A dry well can be of any size, according to circumstances, and it can be made crudely, or somewhat more elaborately. Here is a very simple way of making one:

Dig a hole two to four feet deep and two to three feet in diameter. Make the sides vertical, and if the soil is very loose, line it with brick. Fill the hole to within six or eight inches of the top with large stones loosely packed. Paint a piece of hardware cloth (quarter-inch galvanized mesh) with roofing cement (tar) to prevent its rapid deterioration in contact with damp earth and put it over the stones. Put a layer of gravel, sand and lime over the hardware cloth, and finally a layer of soil. The purpose of the mesh, gravel, sand and lime is to prevent the soil from packing down between the stones. The grade of the surrounding area should be pitched slightly towards the well.

It may be convenient to make the dry well close to the downspout, or it may be necessary to have it some feet distant. If it is not close to the water spill, a pipe should connect the downspout with a drain a few inches below the surface running into the well. The drain can be of tile, or simply a sloping trench filled with stone along which the water can run.

Dry wells are also useful for conserving moisture. By directing a flow of water towards a dry well in an area where there is too much sub-surface drainage, the water is held for a time and seeps out slowly through the walls of the well.

The puddle at the end of a steep walk, or at the bottom of a flight of steps, may sometimes be solved with a dry well. It is not uncommon to find a very small dry well in an old garden under the lowest part of a flagged walk, when the flags are thick and have been placed directly on the soil and not on a bed of sand and cinders.

## Water on Steps

If water lies on steps because no wash has been provided, it may be possible to build up the steps with concrete colored to match the existing material. Do the work carefully, to be sure that it does not look patched, and don't finish the job until you have allowed a little of the new, colored concrete to dry; it is hard to tell when it is wet whether it will be a good match.

If the trouble is a depression worn by time in a patch of soft natural rock, you may have to replace the slab, or to raise it and turn it over.

When a retaining wall is becoming weakened because there is no way for water to escape, it is usually best to call in an expert to find out if and how the situation can be corrected.

## Old Houses

In an old house, when there is existing paving right up to the walls of the house, don't be too impulsive about removing the paving to make planting areas. Remove one or two slabs and check the situation by pouring a few pails of water into the exposed earth. If there is a potential problem, leave the paving to protect the walls and either plant in movable containers, or wall in a planting area on top of the paving. Put plenty of stones or other drainage material at the bottom of the walled-in area, and provide holes at the base for water to drain out onto the exposed paving *away* from the house.

## Water-Logged Soil

Soil may retain water beyond the point of safety for a number of plants because of:

(a) its intrinsic character;
(b) hardpan or some other impervious condition just below the surface;
(c) a grading condition that causes water from a higher level to accumulate.

When poor porosity is caused by heavy, clayey soil, the remedy is to use plenty of soil conditioners, such as sand, peat moss, and lime, and to work them into the soil until a satisfactory consistency has been obtained.

Hardpan is a hardened or cemented layer of soil, which may occur at any depth below the surface. It presents a much more knotty problem than soil that is merely heavy, and the answer may be to grow mainly plants that don't mind wet feet, or that are so shallow-rooted that they will not be troubled by poor drainage below the surface.

For plants that demand good drainage, treat isolated areas by breaking up the hardpan and getting a good depth of well-drained soil. Roses, for instance, must have good deep drainage, and if there is any doubt at all about the subsoil conditions in your garden, apply the rough and ready test for digging a hole about eighteen inches deep and filling it with water.

No two people agree on how quickly the hole should be empty. I would feel uneasy if it were not empty in an hour, but in hot dry areas slow drainage may be an advantage. The point is that for most plants the water must drain out. Even in gardens where the drainage is generally good, there may be isolated pockets of stagnation caused by a buried boulder or slab of stone, so it is really always wise to be on guard when planting fairly deep-rooted material that will be injured by excessive water.

The accumulation of water in a low-lying area often calls for subterranean drainage of some kind, and it is best to consult a local expert, or to get from the library or the State Agricultural Extension Service in your area information about the various methods of constructing sub-surface drainage systems. These are not necessarily complicated.

At the opposite end of the scale from water-logged soil is the condition in which water drains too freely. If this is due to the quality of the soil, work in water-holding materials. These are discussed in the chapter on soil.

In conclusion, don't forget that there are plants for almost every kind of situation; if you don't want to drain the bog, make a bog garden; and if you prefer not to recondition a patch of super-porosity, study the flora of the desert and the dunes. Whether you bend with the wind, or resist its direction, is partly up to you.

# Chapter VIII

# *SOIL*

Soil, the medium in which plants are grown, is anything but a fixed commodity, a static, inert thing. In a country as big and diverse as the United States, there are so many different kinds of soil that a gardener moving from one section to another may very well have to get used to totally different growing conditions. And within huge areas in which the soil is predominantly deep or shallow, rich or sterile, light or heavy, acid or alkaline, are innumerable pockets that deviate from the type, sometimes in an obvious way, and sometimes in ways that become apparent to the layman only through the response of individual plants.

The important thing to remember is that soil can be controlled, whereas many factors that influence plant growth cannot. Heavy soils can be made porous, and light soils can be conditioned to retain mosture. Sterile soils can be rendered fertile, and acidity and alkalinity can be reversed. *Color has absolutely nothing to do with fertility.* A gardener is rarely justified for laying the blame for a poor garden on the soil; rather he should blame himself for growing the wrong kind of plants for the soil he has, or for not doing the things necessary to make it produce the kinds of plants he wants.

In small gardens, especially city gardens, in areas that have been cultivated for generations, the soil has probably not only received different kinds of treatment, sometimes good and sometimes bad, but over the years new soil from a number of places has been introduced, either as topsoil or around the balled and burlapped roots of plants. A small garden with a history of piecemeal handling may be a museum of soil types.

This matter of possible soil variation within a very small area, either as a result of natural conditions or through the work of man, cannot be too strongly stressed; it is at once an irritation, because it adds to the uncertainty of gardening, and a promise, because, within limits, the secrets of its potential are not known. Everyone has experienced a stubborn spot in the garden that refuses to produce in the way one wants it to; over and over again one hears the phrase, "My rose was doing wonderfully until I moved it, and now it isn't happy at all"; or, "This peony is fine, but the one over there, that went in at the same time, is miserable." And though a number of things may be responsible for the difference, it is nevertheless true that the cause *can* lie in a minute variation in the soil.

*The first point* the beginning gardener should remember, therefore, is that advice about soil treatment can never be precise, and that he cannot apply a formula and be done with it. The soil will be with him as long as he gardens, and even if he inherits a productive patch, he will have to cultivate and water and maintain the level of fertility required by the plants he grows.

*The second point* to remember is more encouraging. Whatever the growing conditions in any given area, certain plants almost always thrive. These can be used for the basic planting.

Also, in any community, there are individual gardeners whose plants are outstanding. The new gardener should observe which plants do well, and, if he has an opportunity, find out from the successful gardener what he does to his soil. There is nothing more interesting than to study the methods of a person who has tilled his plot lovingly and fruitfully for a long period. His practice is often empirical, but though he may be hard put to give the reasons for its success, or may produce reasons that sound irrational, you may be sure that if all the data were assembled there would be a solid foundation for his program.

The quickest way to determine the fertility of the soil in one's garden is to have samples analyzed. Most agricultural experiment stations do this for a modest fee. Private laboratories charge more, but the sum is not excessive and the report is usually more detailed. The soil test report is accompanied by recommendations for the use of fertilizer. A soil test protects the gardener from plunging blindly with soil that is toxic or seriously deficient in an element essential to plant growth. It also protects him from spending money on fertilizer he doesn't need, and perhaps damaging his garden by upsetting an already excellent balance. The supposition that if a little is good, more is better, does not apply to fertilizing the garden.

Many gardeners do not want to bother with soil analyses, and for them the advice is either to stick to plants with a wide tolerance, or to proceed cautiously and not buy a lot of unusual and expensive plants until they have tried out their garden, or are reasonably certain from the condition of existing plants and the experience of neighbors that they will not be in trouble. The city gardener should be especially cautious in this respect.

## Topsoil

Some gardeners don't feel safe unless they buy topsoil, but to buy it in quantity is very expensive. There is so much misunderstanding about topsoil that it merits discussion.

In any conversation about plants, the first thing that the average new gardener mentions is topsoil. This is particularly true of the city and suburban gardener in the eastern section of the country. The tenacity with which he embraces what has become a catchword is a tremendous tribute to the promotion drive of the persons who make a business out of scraping the top layer of soil off one part of the land and transporting it to another. There are times when one is tempted to think of topsoil salesmen as bulldozer parasites, battening on the home owner whose parcel of land has been stripped for building and who may never again see the like of what was removed.

The term "topsoil" is at best a general one, used in different ways even by specialists. *Soil,* one of the authoritative yearbooks published by the United States Department of Agriculture, cites four meanings, of which the first is: "A presumed fertile soil or soil material, usually rich in organic matter, used to topdress roadbanks, lawns and gardens." This is the sense in which it is commonly used by home gardeners. There is no question about the value of good topsoil; the thing that is alarming is the aura of magic that has come to surround the word. Any bag of earth so labeled is believed to fill the bill; the source of origin is not questioned because the consumer often does not know that topsoil is of greatly variable quality. And in cities, where soot and noxious fumes are among the gardener's chief handicaps, the new soil, even if it is of excellent quality, is no more resistant to harmful deposits than the soil already there; it is only a matter of time before it, too, becomes polluted.

The advice therefore is, *Don't buy topsoil unless you are sure you need it, and then buy it only from a reputable source.*

## Acidity and Alkalinity

The United States is divided by a line running roughly through the center of the country from north to south that is known as the "lime line." East of this line, soil is predominantly acid; west of the line, soil is predominantly alkaline. There are, of course, many pockets in the generally acid region which are alkaline, and vice versa. In most cities, soil is acid.

The significance of acidity and alkalinity for the gardener is that certain plants have a marked preference for one or the other type of soil. Other plants have a wide tolerance for both.

The degree of alkalinity and acidity in soil is expressed in garden literature by a numerical designation known as the pH. A soil with a pH of 7.0 is neutral; figures above 7.0 indicate increasing alkalinity; figures below 7.0, increasing acidity. The pH index is used with great frequency in books about plants, and it is therefore important to understand it, and to realize that a plant with a strong preference for acid soil cannot be expected to thrive in an alkaline soil, and that alkaline-loving plants will not take kindly to an acid soil.

It is possible to make an acid soil alkaline by the addition of lime, and to create acid conditions in an alkaline soil by the addition of sulphur. In this way plants with totally opposite requirements, such as lilac and holly, can be grown side by side, but the gardener must decide whether he wants to give himself this extra trouble, or whether he prefers plants with a natural compatibility. The science of ecology is concerned in part with plant compatibility and anyone who observes the natural grouping of plants in the wild is a student of ecology. The more artificial gardening becomes, the farther it departs from the laws of ecology and the more work it is for the gardener.

Valuable chapters in the U.S.D.A. Soil Yearbook mentioned above list shrubs and trees requiring acid soil, and give the optimum pH requirements for a number of vegetables.

*Photograph by Bill Graham*

Plate 5.   A glimpse into the garden of Mrs. T. Leslie Samuel, Jr.,
Montgomery, Alabama. Note the well-proportioned wall and the
charming tracery of vine. Ivy is trained on a frame in the flower
pot. The garden is at the rear of a small city lot.

Plate 6. A detail in the garden of Mr. and Mrs. Marion Baxley, Montgomery, Alabama. Note how skillfully the tool shed is built into the design, becoming a visual anchor for the wall and setting off its light, open quality. Note also the excellent proportions of the steps, the crispness of the brick edgings to the beds, the tasteful choice of plants and their rhythmic placing. A chunky little evergreen at the extreme left gives definition to the end of the bed; the same plant at each side of the steps is a pleasing repetition and accents the change in level. Its effect near the steps is enhanced by contrast with the broad planes of caladium leaves and the gray spikes of rosemary. The delicate flowers of the restrained vine on the wall are effective minor accents. The entire planting picture is quiet and restful and yet full of interest. A final charming touch is the graceful iron ornament on the roof of the tool shed. All too seldom does one see such first-rate structural design and fine finish so well coordinated. The result is a garden of distinction.

*Photographs Plates 6 and 7 by Bill Graham*

Plate 7.   Walled patio in the garden of Mr. and Mrs. John Britton, Montgomery, Alabama. The handsome white gate is the entrance from the front yard. Doors at the back of the house open onto the patio. Note the interesting texture of the planting, with large-leafed material framing the pool and the attractive fountain.

*By courtesy of Jackson and Perkins Company; photograph by R. E. Briggs*

Plate 8.   The severity of a plain iron fence and a stark white wall are softened by a dressy planting of roses at a cellar entrance.

## Soil Preparation

Soil preparation involves the addition of nutrients in which it is deficient, and the production of a good tilth, that is, a friable condition in which the roots can obtain the air they need. Soil should *never* be worked when it is sticky wet; to do so puddles it and damages the structure in such a way that it may lose its porosity.

The depth to which soil should be prepared depends upon the kind of garden it is proposed to make. The gardener who expects to enjoy the fruits of his toil during only a brief residence, and the city gardener who wants a little green around him but has neither time nor energy for an ambitious project, need not be frightened away from the idea of a garden by the prospect of deep digging over the entire lot. You can have a garden with only shallow preparation, but your choice of plants will be limited. This is the important point to grasp. Many disappointments stem from a haphazard plant selection—shallow-rooted, deep-rooted, lime-loving, acid-loving material, all together in one small bed which has received uniform treatment, or no treatment at all.

An important piece of advice is, therefore: *Decide on the kind of garden you want to have,* and the amount of effort you are prepared to put into it, before you embark on your soil program.

## Soil Conditioners

The following materials help to produce the physical conditions that make soil productive:

PEAT MOSS. This is a particularly valuable organic soil builder for gardeners dependent on packaged products. Neither a maximum nor a minimum use is recommended; it is probably impossible to use too much, and it is equally true that excellent gardens are made without it. Put simply, peat moss makes gardening, especially gardening in small places, easier. Mixed with the soil it improves the physical condition immediately. Used as a mulch, it is protective in winter and in summer it helps to conserve moisture, *provided the soil below it is not allowed to dry out.* Finally, it makes an aesthetic contribution;

its rich red-brown color is pleasing and a new garden with many bare spots takes on a well-groomed look if it is liberally mulched with peat moss.

Peat moss is sold in 50- and 100-lb. bales and in bags of varying size. Baled peat must be broken up before use. It has a somewhat acid reaction, and if it is used for lime-loving plants a handful of lime should be added to about every pail of peat. If peat moss is mixed with the soil dry, it will absorb an enormous amount of moisture required by plants, and for this reason it should be dampened before use. If the bale can be left outdoors in a concealed spot, the rain will generally insure that a layer is always moist and ready for easy handling. For a mulch, peat moss may be spread on dry and wet down with the sprinkler. Sprinkling should be done immediately, because peat moss freshly loosened from the bale is very light and will quickly blow away.

Michigan peat is used for the same purpose as peat moss but its form is different; it is dark in color and always moist. It does not require breaking or wetting before use, but it is heavier and more expensive in terms of bulk. It is available in plastic bags of varying size.

SAWDUST.   Sawdust and wood shavings are valuable for improving the physical condition of the soil. Even in cities, lumber yards often sell potato sacks of clean sawdust, weighing around ten to fifteen pounds. When a floor is scraped, the last scraping is usually free of paint or varnish; it should not be thrown away but put on the garden.

Sawdust may be used as a mulch or worked right into the soil, but wood shavings are best put on the ground as a mulch, so that they may break down more rapidly. When they have decayed, they may be hoed into the soil.

If wood refuse is used in any quantity, it is advisable to apply fertilizer with a high nitrogen analysis at the same time. This is to counteract the theft of nitrogen by soil organisms that break down the sawdust. And if the plants in the bed to which it is applied are not acid-loving plants such as azaleas and rhododendrons, mix a little lime with it too.

NEWSPAPER.   Newspaper is essentially wood pulp, and though it is troublesome to tear it up and wet it down, it is a very good soil conditioner, if supplemented with the nitrogen mentioned in the previous paragraph. Mr. R. B. Farnham, Executive Secretary of the Horticultural Society of New York, Inc., suggests its inclusion in a compost pit by anyone who has the patience to prepare it. There are cases of shore gardens that have been made productive by the use of newspaper and nothing else.

LEAVES. Rotted leaves and the needles of conifers are splendid for adding humus to the soil. Oak leaves and most conifers have an acid reaction and are especially good for acid-loving plants. Pine needles and the foliage of many broad-leafed trees are neutral. When rotted leaves are not available, and there is no compost pit, leaves can be used as a mulch and gradually incorporated with the soil. In cities in the North, many people collect discarded Christmas trees and put twigs and small branches round their plants. This protects the plants in cold weather, and the appearance of a dreary little city yard in which needle-leaf evergreens will not grow is improved. By spring the needles are becoming loose and ready to break down. The winter use of Christmas greens in a tiny yard also imparts a fragrance which lasts well into the summer.

ANIMAL MANURE. Whenever a stable is handy (and there are still a few stables even in cities and suburbs), the opportunity to get stable manure should be grasped. The fresh manure may be spread thinly over the beds, not touching the plants, where it will dry very quickly. Or it may be covered lightly right away. When the manure dries it can be left as a mulch, or worked into the soil. Stable manure sometimes contains a good deal of bedding straw. This does not decay as quickly as the manure. It makes a good mulch, but is rather unsightly in summer because of the long time it takes to break down. If possible, it should be piled in a concealed place to rot, and later spread and worked into the soil.

Fresh or "green" cow manure may be used in the way described in the preceding paragraph for fresh horse manure. A few bags of cow manure are a truly miracle commodity, and are especially valuable in early spring, when, after the long night of winter, the whole garden seems hungry. If cow manure can be bought in fall and left outdoors all winter, it is in splendid condition to be worked deep into the holes for spring planted shrubs.

Dried and pulverized cow, sheep and pig manures are sold in bags of varying size. They are less valuable as soil conditioners than for making liquid manure to give a boost to a plant. Liquid manure is made by letting a handful or two of dried manure steep overnight or longer in water. A large watering can is a suitable receptacle. If the manure is tied in a piece of burlap it will not clog the strainer of the can when it is applied. The solution should be light brown in color.

RACKS. These are the carcasses of fish from which filets have been cut. Anyone living near a fish business will have no difficulty in obtaining racks. For obvious reasons, they should be covered immediately, and it is generally advisable to get only a small quantity at a time. The best way to use them is at the bottom of a hole in which shrubs or trees are to be planted.

KITCHEN SCRAPS. For those who cannot have a compost pit, kitchen scraps, particularly bones and vegetable refuse, may be incorporated directly in the soil. Fat should be avoided. When there is no problem with invading cats or dogs, refuse may be simply spread on the soil around plants, in such a way that the foliage conceals it. Burying refuse delays decomposition.

SAND. Sand is useful in a number of ways, and a bag should always be on hand in the average garden. Mixed with the top inch or two of soil in a seed bed, it prevents the soil from packing around the young seedlings. If it is used to cover seed sown in drifts or patches in a border, the light color shows up and identifies the seeded areas before germination. It is useful in a bulb planting, where, if mixed with the soil at the bottom of the bulb hole or trench, it helps to provide a well-drained bed for the bulbs. It is invaluable in potting mixtures, and it is extremely useful for striking some kinds of cuttings. Many hardware stores sell bags of sand weighing about fifty pounds. If large quantities of sand are needed, it may be bought by the cubic yard from dealers. If there is any danger of its being salty, it should be washed. This can be done by putting some in a pail, filling the pail with water, letting the sand settle, and pouring off the water. This should be done two or three times.

## Fertilizers

Though some of the materials mentioned above contain valuable plant nutrients, their main purpose is to build up the soil into a good physical condition. In this respect, they are equally valuable on heavy and on light soils. For healthy growth, however, plants require a balanced ration of food. A deficiency of essential ingredients produces varying effects, more pronounced in some plants than in others.

A type of fertilizer known as a complete fertilizer, because it contains the three major ingredients required for plant growth, is available, usually in five, ten, twenty-five and fifty-pound bags. Each bag is stamped with the analysis of the contents, which varies with the kind of plants for which the fertilizer is recommended. The figures in the analysis are always three, and refer, in the order in which they are given, to the percentage of nitrogen, phophorus and potash in the carrier. The analyses most used in ordinary garden work are 5:10:5 and 6:10:4.

Most complete fertilizers are a mixture of organic and chemical material. Organic fertilizer makes a permanent contribution to the soil; chemical fertilizer supplies plants with elements they need for growth but does not build up the soil. Persons who object to the use of fertilizer that is chemically processed are known as "organic" gardeners.

Chemical fertilizer may be sprinkled lightly over the ground to be spaded, or worked into the soil around established plants, or applied as a surface dressing and watered in. It may also be mixed with the soil at the bottom of the hole in which shrubs or trees are to be planted. It should not be allowed to touch the foliage of plants, or to come directly in contact with the roots. In applying this type of fertilizer, the general rule is that it is better to use too little than too much; don't be a heavy-handed cook if your salt is chemical manure.

The three major ingredients of a complete fertilizer, i.e., nitrogen, phosphorus and potash, are also available separately, both in organic and inorganic forms, but the inexperienced gardener is usually wise to avoid this somewhat more specialized method of feeding.

This caution does not, however, apply to the use of certain organic materials that are packaged like chemical fertilizer.

Three kinds especially valuable to the home gardener are bonemeal, dried blood and cottonseed meal.

Bonemeal is exactly what the name implies, finely ground bones, and it is a slow acting, long lasting, and valuable source of phosphoric acid. It is of particular benefit to bulbs. Applied to shrubs and trees in late fall and early and mid-winter, it is ready for the plants when they come to life in spring. No home gardener should be without it.

Dried blood is dark in color and its strong odor is claimed by some to repel animals. It does not appear to be a deterrent to the average alley cat. It is a valuable source of nitrogen.

Cottonseed meal is a fine yellow meal that is pleasant to handle and rich in nitrogen. It is used for plants with a strong acid preference, such as azaleas and rhododendrons.

## Lime

Lime corrects acidity, but it is important to remember that a number of choice broad-leaf evergreens demand an acid soil and would be seriously injured by lime. Besides correcting acidity, lime helps to loosen soil and make it workable, to release certain elements required for plant growth, and to remove the stagnant, sour quality often present in damp city yards. In time-honored language, it "sweetens" the soil.

Kinds of lime available are hydrated lime (used by plasterers) and ground limestone. Hydrated lime is more caustic, somewhat fluffy, and less pleasant to use than ground limestone. The general advice is that hydrated lime should not be used at the same time as fertilizer, but that ground limestone may be. The way to use lime is to sprinkle it on the ground before spading until the area looks as though there has been a light fall of snow. When planting lime-loving shrubs in an acid garden, it should be thoroughly mixed with the soil at the bottom of the hole and with soil used to fill the hole.

In conclusion, the only way to become knowledgeable about soil is to handle it. New gardeners tend to fall into two groups: those who ignore the soil altogether, and those who fuss too much. The first kind never lift a hoe, and then wonder why delicate things suffocate in a medium with the consistency of cement. The second kind are so zealous in their ministrations that the plant is in the position of an over-medicated child.

## Chapter IX

# TERRACES, WALKS, STEPS, WALLS, FENCES

Most things can be done in more than one way, and the difference is not necessarily between good and bad work. Sometimes a method that would be rough under one set of conditions is perfectly acceptable under another. And even in fine work, practice varies under different conditions and between different artisans. A book could be written about any one of the subheads in this chapter.

The home owner proposing to do elaborate work is urged to refer to one of the excellent handbooks available in libraries and bookstores that describe all phases of construction in great detail. The purpose of these notes is to suggest designs and materials, and to refer to a few points that are controversial, and to others that are often overlooked.

### Terraces

When a terrace is to have rough or constant use, economy at the time of making it is rarely economy in the long run. Gravel, crushed stone and grass are relatively inexpensive, but gravel and crushed stone are poor surfaces for garden furniture, besides being easy to track into the house. Grass needs constant attention, and, in a much used area, can be a source of domestic friction, when the gardener's plea to keep off it during periods of renovation falls on deaf ears. For a temporary surface, if the budget does not permit permanent paving, tanbark is an excellent material; it does not become sticky when it is wet and it is pleasing to look at.

WOOD. Wood can be a very satisfactory paving material, and Californian garden literature is lavishly illustrated with pictures of handsome outdoor floor designs in redwood. An ob-

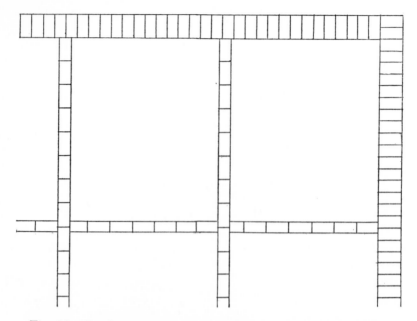

Fig. 10. In this terrace, which is edged with common brick, panels approximately 5' x 5'9" are defined in brick. The panels can be of brick in a basketweave or false herringbone pattern, of cut flagstone, or of concrete.

jection to the type of wood flooring in which the boards are spaced and raised is that pointed heels catch; it is also amazing how many articles can slip through a small crack.

Wooden blocks set directly on the earth, unless packed very close together and tamped absolutely level, are difficult to sweep. This type of paving is often pictured with an appreciable earth-filled gap between blocks; this may not be satisfactory for an outdoor living room close to the house. When wooden block paving is used, it should be edged with a strong curb to hold it firmly in place and prevent individual blocks from becoming loose. The curb may be of stone, brick, boards, logs, or wooden blocks set on end.

Occasionally one sees an outdoor wood terrace paved with blocks cut hexagonally by some craftsman long ago and fitted as closely and carefully as ceramic tile. I saw such a paving in Australia, made of jarrah. After a hundred years, it was flawless. Only the most rot-resistant lumber, such as locust, bald cypress (*Taxodium*) and perhaps some grades of redwood,

Figs. 11 and 12. Designs for paving with common brick laid on 8″ x 4″ face.

would be suitable for this type of paving. Indeed, it is questionable whether it would be particularly appropriate for an outdoor living room, but it is an interesting example of the use to which wood is sometimes put.

Cross-sections of lumber make delightful flooring for an informal terrace. Rot-resistant wood, such as bald cypress, western white cedar, redwood, or locust should be used. A wood preservative is generally recommended for any wood except cypress that is to be in contact with the soil.

A foundation is not necessary for wood paving in mild climates or on sandy soil, but when the soil is heavy and winter heaving is a problem, a foundation of several inches of broken stone or gravel overlaid with sand is advisable.

The most durable materials for paving a terrace are brick, native stone, cut or broken flagstone, and concrete.

BRICK. Brick is somewhat tedious to lay, but it possesses a quality that is lacking in every other material and its appearance improves with age. In fact, probably no paving material mellows more handsomely with age, and it is positively difficult to make work with old weathered brick look shoddy. When it is wet, the color is rich and satisfying and the texture never clammy. Since it does not radiate heat, it is good for hot cli-

Figs. 13 and 14. Designs for paving with blocks or bricks having a 12″ x 4″ face. Common building bricks cannot be used for this paving.

mates. In cold climates, it looks much warmer than slate-colored flagstone.

The difference between brick laid dry on a bed of sand, overlying a bed of cinders or gravel, and brick laid in mortar, may be compared to the difference between hand-woven and machine-made cloth, and there are landscape architects who engage in a perpetual battle with masons and clients who want every bit of brickwork laid in mortar. However, when the floor is to be used for dancing, or when there are children with roller skates and tricycles, the use of mortar is necessary. The point to remember is that the two methods produce a totally different effect and that when traffic is heavy another type of paving may be preferable.

Bricks laid dry should be packed as tightly as possible. Even with sand brushed into the cracks, the bricks will wobble if they are not laid tight; also, the sand washes out and is objectionable. The edging must be absolutely solid. If it is made of brick, it may be advisable to use mortar for the marginal course; much depends upon the amount of traffic.

The foundation for bricks laid in mortar should be three to four inches thick. Don't, however, lay the bricks directly on a "sloppy wet" foundation; it will be almost impossible to keep the surface of the bricks even. Instead, roughen the surface of the foundation and allow it to set. Then spread a mixture of two parts of sand and one part of cement over the foundation, in a layer about an inch thick. Sprinkle the sand-cement mixture lightly with water, a small area at a time, and lay the bricks on it, packing them tight and tamping each one carefully in place. Fill the cracks with the same mixture, and wash off the excess. The sand-cement mixture will bond with the underlying concrete and set into a rigid base for the brick. When the whole terrace is laid, clean off any fragments of mixture still adhering to the surface with muriatic acid.

When you are laying the bricks, keep the pattern straight by putting a line of cord across the terrace from one side to the other, pegging it firmly. Follow the line as you would if you were planting vegetable seed.

STONE.    Stone can be random rectangular flagstone, broken flagstone, or native stone.

Flagstones vary a great deal in thickness. Heavy stones three inches and more thick may be laid directly on the earth even in severe climates. Thinner flags laid dry should have a base of sand overlying gravel or cinders.

Flagstones laid dry must be packed very tightly to prevent grass growing between the cracks. No matter how tightly they are laid, however, the heels fashionable today are so pointed that they have a tendency to catch. If the terrace is to be used for dancing, this may be a serious objection.

If cement is used, the *thorough* way is to lay the stone in a concrete bed, but many masons simply pour mortar, which can be colored to match the stone, between the cracks. Since the mortar may be expected to crack as the large stones settle, and during periods of thawing and freezing, perfectionists regard this practice with horror; but it is much less expensive and much simpler than laying the flags in a concrete bed, and it is easy to repair cracks with ready-mix concrete.

Admittedly, a flagstone terrace in which cement is used does not have the fine, hand-made look of one laid dry, but if the work is carefully done, the effect is not displeasing.

Irregular pieces of flagstone are almost impossible to use for a terrace without cement, unless the area is very rough. It is much more difficult to make a good-looking paving with broken flagstone than with random rectangular pieces. Broken flagstone and native stone laid dry are most satisfactory when the spaces are filled with mat-like plants.

CAST STONE. Pre-cast concrete blocks of irregular size are much pleasanter to look at than a smooth unbroken surface of concrete. Whenever concrete is used, however, the appearance of the terrace is improved if some other material is introduced. Bricks or wooden blocks can be used to make an interesting pattern. If they are laid first, they will serve as forms for the concrete mix.

One of the most effective materials to combine with concrete is a coarse aggregate made of pebbles set in a concrete mix. This is especially recommended in areas where the soil yields quantities of smooth pebbles of a suitable size and color. This condition often exists near the shore, in sections that have been under glaciation, and in old river valleys. The coarse-aggregate blocks can be pre-cast, or made at the same time as the terrace. They require more patience, of course, than a plain concrete surface; but properly used they give dignity and distinction to what might otherwise be a very dull paving.

TANBARK, PINE NEEDLES, WOOD CHIPS. All these materials make a pleasing floor for an outdoor living room. Remove any stones from the area to be covered, level it, roll or tamp it, and cover it to a thickness of about two inches with the paving material.

Brick, board and railway ties make good edgings for this type of paving.

Figure 43 shows an outdoor living room surfaced with tanbark in which an area large enough for a table and chairs has been laid in brick. The entire area is edged with brick.

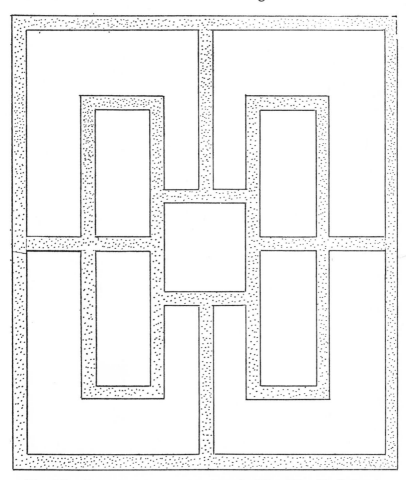

Fig. 15.   Concrete terrace approximately 19′ x 22′ with design in dark-colored coarse aggregate mix (pebble finish concrete). The coarse aggregate can be pre-cast in blocks, or laid in forms at the same time as the terrace. The dark-colored bands are 8″ wide. Common brick can be used instead of aggregate.

THE PITCH OF A TERRACE.    A pitch that is too steep makes for tilting garden furniture, and the irritation of liquid spilling out of containers set on a sloping table top. The pitch should not exceed two and one-half inches in ten feet. I once allowed myself to be bullied by a mason into making a patio at the end of a small garden with a pitch of five inches in twelve feet. I protested, but he was experienced and very determined. When the job was finished, I asked him why he had been so insistent. He replied with Latin excitement, "My patio, no one would see my patio!" I realized he was so proud of his work that he would have stood it on end if he could. The slope of the table on the patio was not good, but still not impossible, and the slight exaggeration of the pitch did actually play up the area and increase the apparent size of the garden slightly.

The purpose of the pitch, of course, is to allow water to drain off smoothly and fairly rapidly. In a big job, elevations are established by surveying instruments, but on small properties, simple, rule-of-thumb methods often suffice. An easy way of laying out a small paved area is the following:

After staking out the terrace, dig a trench round the whole area, about three inches deep on the high side and a little deeper on the low side. Sink a frame of two by four lumber into the trench. Use a mason's or carpenter's level to be sure that the sides of the frame are level. Place a board (piece of rigid lumber) across the frame, from the high side of the terrace to the low side. (If the terrace is more than about twelve feet wide, it will be necessary to perform this operation in more than one step, and establish the grade at, say, ten-foot intervals.) Place the level on the board and, resting one end of the board on the frame at the high side of the terrace, adjust the board until it is level. Prop it in this position, and adjust the low side of the frame to the required pitch. If the pitch is to be two inches in ten feet, and the terrace is ten feet wide, the low side of the frame should be two inches below the high side; if the terrace is fifteen feet wide, the difference in level will be three inches and so on. When the frame has been adjusted, make it firm by driving stakes into the ground. You now have a frame into which to fit the terrace.

If the terrace is to be made of heavy flagstone, three or more inches thick, without a cushion of cinders and sand, prepare the soil within the frame by removing all stones near the surface and raking it smooth. If it has been necessary to work it deeply, let it settle for a few days. In any case, tamp it. When it is thoroughly settled, begin putting the flags in place. Prepare the bed for each flag separately by raking lightly and mixing in a little sand if the soil is heavy.

Begin at the upper side of the terrace and place the first stone so that its upper edge is resting against the frame and level with it. Then take the piece of board and rest it across the frame and the flagstone. It should touch squarely the surface of the stone and the top and bottom sides of the frame. Continue in this way, testing the position of each stone as it is placed, until the whole terrace has been laid.

Use your eye to decide on a pleasing pattern, and try to avoid joints that continue in a straight line from stone to stone. When the stone varies in color and texture, stones lighter or darker than the majority, or coarser or finer in texture, should be scattered rather than laid all together. When all the stones are in place, test them again with the length of board and adjust or tamp any pieces that are out of position; then brush clean sand into the spaces between the flags.

If the paving material is to be laid on a bed of sand and cinders, excavate within the frame to the required depth to allow for a cushion of cinders or gravel (about six inches) and sand (about two inches). Both the cinder layer and the sand layer should be flooded and tamped.

Whatever material is used to pave the terrace, the frame of two by fours makes it easy to achieve a uniform grade and a smooth surface. If it is necessary to pitch in more than one direction, divide the frame with a center board.

If the terrace is raised above the surrounding level, it should be faced along the exposed sides. Even when the facing stones are heavy, they should be set in concrete. To do this, dig a trench and pour in a footing of concrete. This will hold the facing stones in line. Place one-inch boards along the exposed sides of the terrace and hold them in place with stakes driven into the ground. Put the facing stones in position in front of the board. Pour concrete into the cracks between the facing stones, leaving a few openings for drainage. When the concrete has set, remove the board and pour concrete into the space between the facing and the terrace. Exposed concrete should be colored to match the stone.

## Walks

Walks are primarily a means of getting from one part of the garden to another, but they are also part of the design of the garden and they should not receive second-rate treatment any more than should the hallways in a house. The front walk usually leads to the entrance hall, and is its outdoor counterpart; it is also the transition area from the street to the house just as a terrace is a transition from the house to the garden. It is therefore proper to consider its treatment in relation to both street and house.

When the street is a pleasant thoroughfare, with trees and a parking strip between the sidewalk and the road, it is easy to fit the front walk into the picture. A street, however, is not always a park-like place, and a motley of exposed front paths makes the situation worse. What is more, the displeasing character of the street rubs off onto the front garden.

In such a case, heavy planting at the entrance, on both sides if the path leads from the sidewalk, and between the sidewalk and the entrance if the path leads from the drive, is a great improvement, and much more effective than a naked path leading to a planting at the front door. In this way, a feeling of entering a new area is created at the sidewalk.

The front walk, as already stated in the chapter discussing the renovation of an old property, should be of durable material, constructed so that water does not collect in puddles, and generous in width. Even on a very small property, it should if possible be not less than four feet wide. Appropriate materials have been discussed in the chapter on building materials. So far as material goes, much of what has been said about terraces applies to walks. Figures 28 and 29 show designs for front walks.

Secondary paths need not be so wide or so durable as the front walk, and though it is preferable to have them more than three feet wide, so that two people can walk abreast, this may not be convenient on a small property. When paths have to be narrow, corners should always be rounded or flattened, to give a little more width where there is a turn in direction.

When two paths intersect, an elaboration of design at the intersection adds interest. In brick paths, this can be done by

*Designs for Brick Walks*

Figs. 16 and 17, top: Running bond. This pattern is monoto-nous in any but a very short walk if not broken by courses of bricks at right angles to the length of the path. It also makes a narrow path look more narrow.

Fig. 18, bottom left: The double courses of bricks at right angles to the direction of the path may occur at regular or irregular inter-vals. Single courses may be substituted for double courses, but in one path the pattern should be consistent throughout.

Fig. 19, bottom right: Alternate stretcher and header courses make a simple and popular pattern.

Fig. 20, top left:   This pattern gives width to a narrow path.

Fig. 21, top right:   A firm edging is required for all brick paths laid dry. It is especially important when this pattern is used.

Fig. 22, bottom left:   This pattern limits the width of the path to multiples of 16″ (the length of two bricks). To make a 3′ path, a border on each side is necessary. It is more satisfactory for walks at least 4′ wide, and for patio floors.

Fig. 23, bottom right:   The basketweave pattern is simple and popular.

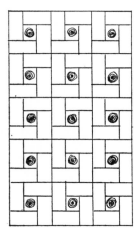 

Fig. 24, top left:   Colored tile is worked into this design, which comes from Spain. The bricks must be uniform in size. A walk in which this design is used should be laid in concrete.

Fig. 25, top right:   The herringbone pattern is better for a wide path than a narrow one.

Figs. 26 and 27, bottom:   The pattern in both these walks is oblique or false herringbone. Note the difference in appearance produced by the direction in which the bricks are laid.

changing the pattern, and/or introducing a rectangle of cut flagstone or a pattern of ornamental tile. In a flagstone path, brick is sometimes suitable for working into the design at an intersection.

STEPS IN A WALK. When it is necessary to have a step in a walk, the pattern of the paving should always indicate a change in level. If this is not done, it is easy to trip on what appears to be a continuing level. This is particularly so in a brick path where the bricks are set in running bond (Figure 17). In a concrete or flagstone path it is difficult to show a change in level unless a different material is used, either for the riser or for an edging to the step. The little extra trouble required to introduce brick or flagstone in a concrete path, or brick in a flagstone path, is, however, well worth while.

Since walks are part of the pattern of the garden, it is well to consider how they will look from the terrace and from upper windows of the house. In cold climates, particularly, when much of the garden is bare for months of the year, it is more satisfactory to look out of the window at a neatly edged path of pleasing color than at a nondescript strip that melts into the planting area.

Generally speaking, walks leading from a terrace should not show an abrupt change in material. At least, there should be some harmony of color and texture between the two surfaces.

EDGINGS. The edging of a walk should be considered in relation to adjacent areas. An informal path in a woodland-type area, where small plants grow between the paving stones and sprawling plants loosely define the planting area, usually doesn't require any edging at all. On the other hand, in a formal area, or near the house, a tailored edging gives crispness and dignity and finish. It is equally necessary whether the walk itself be of durable material set in mortar, or informally surfaced with crushed stone, gravel, grass, tanbark, pine needles or wood chips.

When the walk adjoins a lawn, the edging should of course be flush with the lawn to prevent stumbling. (The edging of a bed set in a lawn is also best made flush with the lawn, to facilitate mowing.)

When a walk adjoins a planting area, part of the function of the edging is to prevent soil from washing onto the walk and to help restrain invasive plants. It should therefore be raised slightly.

If a raised edging is made without mortar, some water from the walk will run off into the bed and relieve the downward wash along the path. If the edging is of concrete, or if mortar is used to build a brick or stone edging, it is sometimes desirable to leave a few openings for side drainage.

## Steps

Since steps are a means of connecting different levels, the first question is, "What is the height and abruptness of the bank?" The answer largely determines whether the steps are to be steep, or whether they are to follow a gentle incline, for, obviously, wide treads with shallow risers occupy much more space than narrow treads with high risers.

The tread is the horizontal part of the step that you "tread" on; the riser is the vertical part between steps. Outdoor steps usually have a broader tread and a lower riser than indoor steps, and a basic rule is, the broader the tread the more shallow the riser. A helpful guide in determining the actual width of the tread and the height of the riser is that *twice the riser plus the tread should equal twenty-six to twenty-seven inches.*

It is usually undesirable for the risers of outdoor steps to exceed six inches, though sometimes the only solution is to make the riser height greater than six inches.

Assuming that the difference in level and the space available calls for a fairly steep ascent, a simple approach to the problem is to divide the difference in grade by six inches. If the difference is three feet, six steps will be required. Remembering the rule that twice the riser plus the tread should equal twenty-six to twenty-seven inches, the steps will call for a tread of fourteen to fifteen inches. The rule may be modified slightly, of course, and it may be necessary to make the tread a little narrower or the riser a little higher, but it is wise to try to keep within an inch of the formula. Everyone must have experienced the muscular discomfort of climbing steps with broad treads and high risers, or the irritation of mincing up a flight of steps with narrow treads and very low risers.

You may have to divide several possible riser heights into the height of the bank before you decide on the right number of steps. And it may be necessary to change the grade a little to get a flight of steps that will fit into a satisfactory design.

All steps should be built with a slight wash or pitch, say one-quarter inch, to permit water to run off.

STYLE.   The determination of how many steps, and how wide and high, may be described as the basic engineering problem. The other questions largely concern style, for, apart from their obvious function as a means of ascent and descent, steps may be played up as a conspicuous feature in the garden, or designed to attract as little attention as possible.

Steps ascending among rocks, and steps in an informal area, should usually be designed to blend as naturally as possible into the rocky face of the slope or the contour of the bank. This does not mean that they should be carelessly made, for safety should always be a first consideration. The material used for the tread should be firm, so that there is no danger of bricks or stones coming loose and causing an accident. Stone should not be too smooth, so that it is slippery and treacherous. If logs or heavy lumber are used as risers, they should be firmly anchored. If the flight is steep, a railing or wing wall should be provided.

STEPS AS ORNAMENT.   The place for "architectural" steps is in a formal part of the garden, or close to the house. The design need not necessarily be elaborate, even if the house is ornate. When I raise my eyes from the typewriter, I look at a picture of a temple in Nara, Japan, and I am struck by the simplicity of the steps. Standing at a little distance, one is confronted by the marvelously curved and elaborately ornate tiled roof and the great beams defining the entrance, and leading to this rich edifice is a gentle flight of wide, light-colored stone steps, with a low simple wing wall on each side. The steps carry the walk up to the temple, rather than the temple down to the walk.

So, too, the steps leading to a dwelling, or from one part of the garden to another, can, to some extent, bring the upper level down, or carry the lower level up. They can also be an individual decorative element, connecting two levels that in themselves lack any particular distinction.

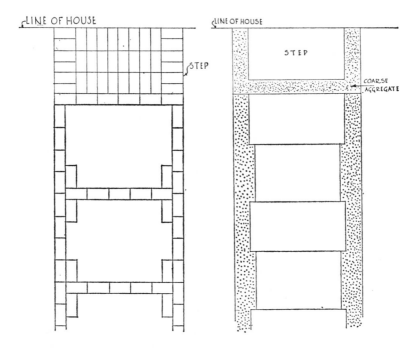

Fig. 28, left:   A front walk 4' wide of brick and concrete with a brick step. The width of the step is 2'4". The concrete of the walk is interrupted at intervals of 2'6" by a course of bricks.

Fig. 29, right:   A front walk 4' wide of concrete blocks or flagstones with a border of coarse aggregate mix (pebble finish concrete). The narrow blocks are 3' x 1'6", with a coarse aggregate edging of 6". The wide blocks are 2'8" x 1'9", with an 8" edging. The width of the step is 2'.

These considerations may sound a little extravagant in relation to the small properties discussed in this book; but, really, they are not, for the basic principles of design apply equally to every object made by man; there is no greatest and no least in this sense. In fact, it may well be argued that, for the individual, the things with which he is in daily association are of greater significance than public edifices with which he has only occasional contact.

MATERIALS.   All the building materials mentioned in Chapter VI, including iron, are suitable for steps. Iron is especially satisfactory for a spiral staircase in a confined area leading from a deck to the garden. In such a case, ironwork is lighter in appearance and less overpowering than steps of any other material. And if the steps descend in front of windows on a lower level, open ironwork will exclude a minimum of light.

When a spiral iron staircase is built in a tiny garden, it almost inevitably becomes a dominant architectural feature, and it should be designed accordingly. The shadows made on the surface below by the pattern of the ironwork will become part of the design. They should not be lost by falling on foliage but should be defined sharply on an unplanted surface.

Tile is often a handsome adornment to steps, but because it is slippery it is better to introduce it on risers and wing walls than on treads, where it could be extremely dangerous. It will also have a better chance of retaining its brightness if it is not subjected to the kind of concentrated wear that is inescapable on treads.

When there is any doubt about what kind of steps to have, the best way to decide is to study photographs. Steps photograph well, and so many beautiful garden staircases have tempted so many expert photographers that pictorial research in this field is especially rewarding.

## Walls

In American gardens today walls have ceased to have a primary function of enclosing the property. Rather, they are much more often adjuncts to the garden, enclosing areas within it, or separating one part from another. As a background to a planting, there is probably nothing to equal them; and when a fairly high wall encloses an entire area, the garden possesses an intimacy and feeling of seclusion that it is difficult to achieve in any other way. This quality is apparent in the patio gardens of California, where the house is built round a courtyard, and in a similar type of garden in old New Orleans. The influence, of course, is Spanish.

In this type of garden, every bit of detail work, and every specimen plant, small or large, produces its maximum effect. Planting can thus be much more varied and interesting, with relatively few individual plants, than in an open area three times the size, where isolated small specimens tend to look

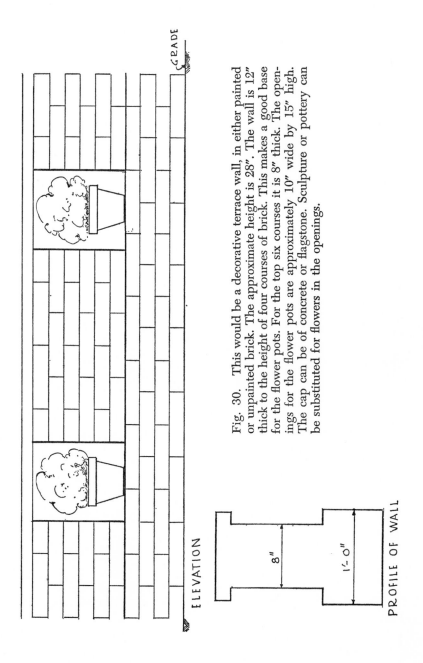

Fig. 30. This would be a decorative terrace wall, in either painted or unpainted brick. The approximate height is 28". The wall is 12" thick to the height of four courses of brick. This makes a good base for the flower pots. For the top six courses it is 8" thick. The openings for the flower pots are approximately 10" wide by 15" high. The cap can be of concrete or flagstone. Sculpture or pottery can be substituted for flowers in the openings.

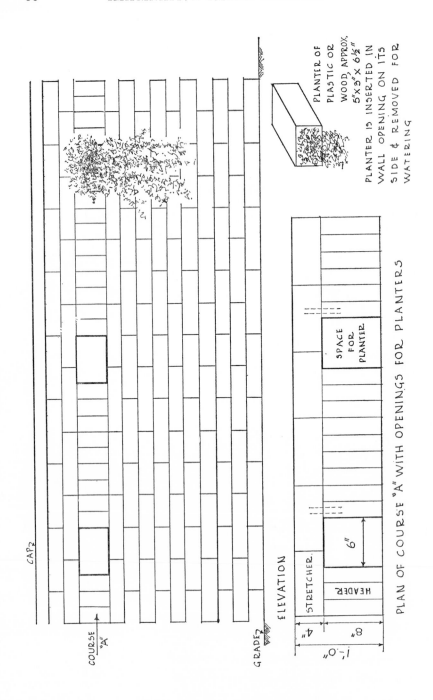

PLANTER OF PLASTIC OR WOOD APPROX. 5" x 3" x 6½"

PLANTER IS INSERTED IN WALL OPENING ON ITS SIDE & REMOVED FOR WATERING

CAP

COURSE "A"

GRADE

ELEVATION

SPACE FOR PLANTER

STRETCHER.

HEADER

6"

4"

8"

1'-0"

PLAN OF COURSE "A" WITH OPENINGS FOR PLANTERS

Fig. 31. An ideal setting for this wall is a background of large shrubs. It can be directly in front of the shrubs, or separated from them by a walk. Used in this way, it gives intimacy to a small area.

The height shown is approximately 3'. It could be greater, but if the wall were too high, it would be troublesome to remove the planters for watering. Unpainted brick is suitable, but brick painted white presents fewer problems in choosing flower colors.

The planting pockets are provided by building a course of headers about two courses below the top of the wall and omitting three or four headers at regular intervals. The space to leave between pockets depends on the length of the wall and the taste of the builder. Too far apart, they might look spotty; it would be better to err on the side of closeness.

The dimensions of the openings in the diagram are approximately 6" wide (three headers) by 4" high by 8" deep. The width can be any measurement the builder likes, but the height and depth are fixed by the size of the brick. Planting boxes of wood or plastic are inserted in the openings.

PLANTS. A number of plants are suitable. Some suggestions:

Small-leafed ivies (*Hedera* species). Shade.

Dittany of Crete *(Origanum dictamnus)*. A tender herb related to the culinary herb, with graceful sprays of gray, woolly leaves. Sun.

Black-eyed clock vine, Black-eyed Susan *(Thunbergia)*. A small trailing annual vine with yellow and cream black-centered flowers. Sun.

Creeping zinnia *(Sanvitalia procumbens)*. Blossoms like miniature sunflowers. Sun.

Leadwort *(Plumbago larpentae)*. Blue flowers. Sun or light shade.

*Lobelia erinus* in variety. Trailing forms preferred. Blue flowers. Sun.

Petunias. Avoid compact varieties. Sun. White varieties are pretty against a natural brick wall.

Portulaca. Sun. A mixture of colors is very gay in a white wall.

Periwinkle *(Vinca minor)*. Well-grown plants of periwinkle provide graceful greenery in shade or sun.

Creeping Charlie *(Lysimachia nummularia)*. Sun or shade. This is a weed in some places, but its little yellow flowers are pretty in spring and the light green leaves are always fresh-looking.

spotty or to get lost altogether. For this reason, every garden should, if possible, have an enclosed area.

It is often not practicable to make a wall high enough to insure the privacy desired in the living area; this can be achieved by large shrubs, which make an excellent background for the type of low wall illustrated in these pages. Then, if the wall is used to enclose the terrace, it serves the double purpose of dressing up the terrace and making a background for flower

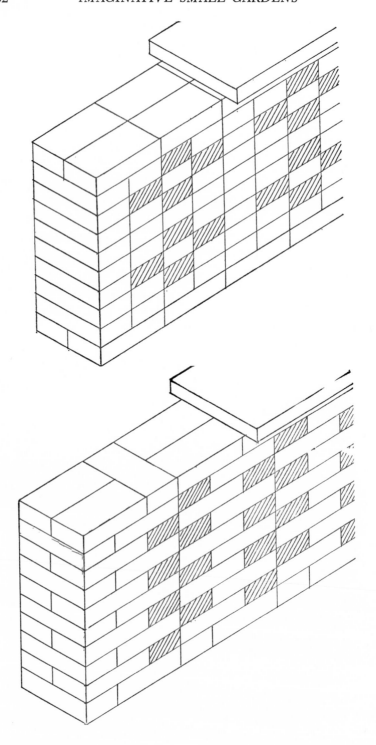

Fig. 32, opposite: Openwork brick wall 8″ thick and approximately 28″ high. The pattern of the openwork, shown by shading, is made by omitting headers. This makes a light wall for a terrace.

Fig. 33, opposite: Another 8″ brick wall, approximately 28″ high, but with a different pattern of openwork. The drawing shows the construction.

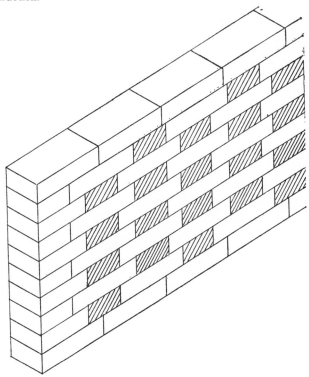

Fig. 34. This openwork wall is 4″, the width of a brick, thick, and about 26″ high. It would be too delicate for a high wall, but is perfectly satisfactory for a low one. The bricks overlap for about 2″, making the dimensions of the openings about 4″ x 2″.

borders adjoining the terrace. If the wall is open, the color of the flower border shows through the lacework of the structure. The openings also permit a delicate clinging vine, such as Low's variety of Boston ivy *(Parthenocissus tricuspidata lowi)*, or a small-leafed English ivy or wintercreeper, to be trained over the inside surface of the wall.

## Fences

The enclosure of the private living area often presents an opportunity to use a well-designed screen fence, the cost of

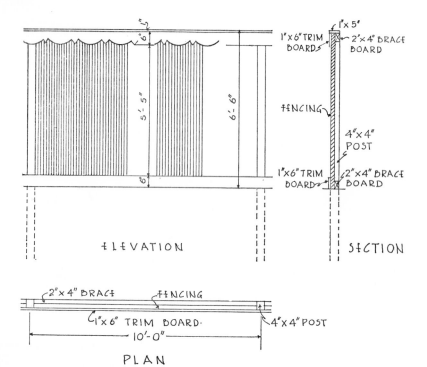

*Two designs for a screen fence, Figs. 35 and 36, by
Mary Deputy Cattell, Landscape Architect*

Fig. 35.   Woven wood fence with top and bottom trim. The trim
can be stained to match the fence, or painted white. It eliminates
the untidy look so often present in a woven wood fence when
palings get out of alignment.

which would be prohibitive around an entire property but
within the budget for a shorter footage. Many stock fences are
available, and these are usually less expensive than a custom-
made fence built to the owner's design. The latter, of course,
are more individual. Two such fences designed by Mary Deputy Cattell, L.A., are shown in Figures 35 and 36. Another appears in Plate 24, following page 192.

### Boundary Treatment

An area of home landscaping that would benefit by thoughtful discussion is boundary treatment.

The European tradition is to enclose all gardens, large or
small, with a fence, wall, or hedge. Many of the large estates

that were landscaped in America at the turn of the century were modeled on famous gardens abroad, and the boundary was defined with an impressive structure in masonry or wood or iron, or planted with an opulent green hedge.

The enclosing of large estates in this way did not, however, reflect a national trend. Early Colonial gardens were fenced, but mainly to protect property from straying animals. When this necessity was removed, the enclosing fence disappeared also.

It may well be that the open grounds of American gardens are the natural expression of a freedom-loving people; certainly the absence of "no trespass" devices round private yards is consistent with the expansive generosity of the American character. Whatever the reason, however, an unenclosed property is more difficult to landscape than one that is fenced, walled, or hedged in.

It is expensive to enclose an entire property, and though one may argue about whether an appropriate enclosure should not have priority over a number of other expenditures the importance of which is never questioned, the practice is so firmly entrenched that it would be unrealistic not to accept it.

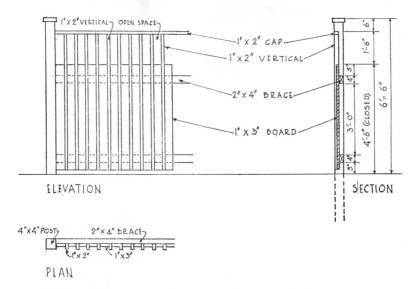

Fig. 36. The fence is closed to a height of 4'. The open top provides partial screening and saves the fence from heaviness.

THE POPULAR ATTITUDE. What is perhaps realistic is an examination of the popular attitude towards boundary treatment. Obviously, the feeling that the entire property, on all four sides, must be screened from the public gaze is outmoded. Just as obviously, very few have surrendered the desire for privacy in the living area. What is apparently unresolved in the minds of many home owners is the delineation of the boundary in the so-called public area. The result is often a general unsureness of treatment, and the impression that whatever has been done has been done as an afterthought and not as part of the general scheme. Sometimes it takes the form of a little dab here and there—unrelated pillars at entrance and corners, or a free-standing arbor.

Perhaps it is this unsureness that is so irritating. One longs to say: "Make up your mind. Do you want a hedge—fence—wall, or don't you?" Quite possibly, the home owner has never really thought about it, and it is equally possible that if he did he would arrive at a satisfactory and logical solution.

For instance, if his garden were much bothered by itinerant domestic animals, he might decide that it would be more sensible to spare himself, once and for all, the anguish of damaged plants and scarred lawns and unneighborly feelings by spending money he had reserved for something else on a good enclosure. Or he might find that he wanted very much to espalier shrubs or grow climbing roses, and that a fence would provide the support he had no room for in any other part of the garden.

Or again, he might, on deliberation, decide that he liked his garden open, enjoyed the view he shared with his neighbors, and had no problems to make him change his mind. The situation would immediately take on a rational aspect.

AN ESSENTIAL PART OF THE DESIGN. The important thing is to consider the boundary treatment, or absence of it, as a fundamental part of garden planning, and not something to be pushed aside, with an uneasy look over one shoulder at an outdated convention, and a vague glance over the other at a half-formed wish.

In arriving at a decision, the character of the street, the house, and surrounding properties should be considered, as well as the appearance of the garden from inside the dwelling.

*John Eyerman, Landscape Architect; photograph by Shan Stewart*

Plate 9. (Plan of garden on page 110, Figure 42.) The roof of the shelter is Fiberglas. The louvered sides between the roof and the top of the fence screen the area from the neighboring house. The ground cover is recently-planted dichondra.

*Dina G. Bauman, Landscape Architect; photographs by Bee Pancoast Weber*

Plan of garden, with description and plant lists, on pages 112, 113 and 114 (Figures 43 and 44).

Plate 10.   Wooden deck leading from kitchen to outdoor living area. The informal espalier is a small, early-flowering hybrid horse-chestnut *(Aesculus).* The shrub at the extreme lower left is *Cotoneaster henryana.*

Plate 11, opposite top:   Seat around pear tree at entrance to living area. The rose at the right is climbing Blaze.

Plate 12, opposite bottom:   Textures on floor of living area.

*Elizabeth Howerton, Landscape Architect; photograph by R. K. Sunder-bruch*

Plate 13. Espaliered Hopa crabapples make a background for a low wall and flower border. (The word espalier has acquired for many people a restricted meaning of woody plants trained against a wall. It is equally accurate to use it for free-standing woody plants trained to a flat and more or less symmetrical shape.) Plan of garden is on page 118.

Plate 14. Steps leading to lower level of garden.

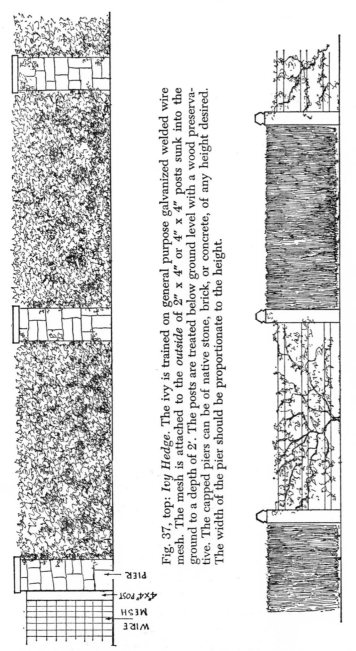

WIRE
MESH
4"X4" POST
PIER

Fig. 37, top: *Ivy Hedge.* The ivy is trained on general purpose galvanized welded wire mesh. The mesh is attached to the *outside* of 2" x 4" or 4" x 4" posts sunk into the ground to a depth of 2'. The posts are treated below ground level with a wood preservative. The capped piers can be of native stone, brick, or concrete, of any height desired. The width of the pier should be proportionate to the height.

Fig. 38, bottom: This clipped hedge alternates with panels of post and rail fence. A vine or shrub is trained against the fence. The hedge and fence can be of any appropriate height.

Figures 37 and 38 show two simple treatments; many more will occur to the person who has become boundary conscious.

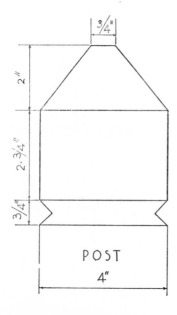

Fig. 39. A simple square finial for a 4″ x 4″ post.

## Seats and Ornaments

The stone benches, and tiled and wrought iron seats that once constituted garden furniture have been largely replaced by the much more comfortable and easily moved equipment that is available today. There is, however, in nearly every garden, a place for a permanent seat, not for lounging but simply for sitting a while. This kind of seat can be extremely ornamental and is particularly pleasing in a rose garden. In Mexico and Spain beautiful seats are made by setting tile in concrete.

If a stone seat is low enough and wide enough, and modeled a little, it can actually be quite comfortable. The best one I ever sat on is in the grounds of the Hedgerow summer stock theater in Media, Pennsylvania. The theater is an ancient mill house, and the seat is built under a silver maple on top of a culvert over a little stream. It is made of rough stone, covered and smoothed with concrete, and the concrete has been "contoured" in the most skillful way. The seat is low, nine to eleven inches, and the proportions are ample, seven feet between the arms and two feet from front to back.

A garden ornament or feature does not have to be a piece of conventional and expensive statuary. It can be anything, from a totem pole to a piece of driftwood or a rock, and America must be one of the most exciting places in the world in which to look for it. Wooden sculpture, Indian pottery, Spanish tile, can all be used with enormous effect. Hand-carved finials in different designs are delightful for the posts of a small enclosure. A hand-carved panel can sometimes be introduced into a gate. Once the garden is made, the addition or changing of minor finishing touches can go on for years and be a most enjoyable hobby.

## Chapter X

# *MAINTENANCE*

Associations with the word maintenance are almost entirely negative, but if the gardener stops to think he will realize that all the happy puttering he does in his garden is part of maintenance. People vary greatly in the kind of garden jobs they enjoy and the kind they find a burden. I remember comparing notes with a friend on this subject. She said that she liked digging and spraying and disliked pruning and handling seed, and I replied that I detested her pet operations but thoroughly enjoyed pruning and loved to grow things from seed. The man who is doing something that interests him does not think of it as a chore, but to another the same thing will be a burdensome part of maintenance.

Another point is the great difference of opinion as to what is objectionable. Those for whom a carpet of flowers from a blossoming tree is an annual delight are usually content to let the petals wither where they fall; others think only of the mess on patio and walks and are out every day with a broom.

The conclusion is obvious: plan a garden that provides maximum scope for the jobs you enjoy and demands a minimum of energy for activities that are distasteful. Of course, no one can have it entirely his way, and the inexperienced gardener may not always know what is going to give him most pleasure. He does, however, know what kind of person he is, and he can consider at the planning stage the future as well as the immediate demands of every feature he contemplates for his garden.

*The factors governing maintenance are therefore implicit in everything that has been said in this book.* Apart from keeping a watchful eye on projects that may turn out to be more than you bargained for, the rest is a simple matter of common sense and good housekeeping. Following is a summary of basic do's and don'ts:

## Architectural Features

Avoid constant repairs by using durable material for permanent structures such as walls, fences, steps and walks and don't permit slipshod construction.

Don't put rock salt on concrete walks and drives; a chemical reaction between the salt and the cement will produce cracking and pitting. (Rock salt is also injurious to plants and should not be allowed to wash into a growing area.)

Use architectural accents such as sculpture, pottery and pieces of natural rock if you want to cut down on plant maintenance.

Remember that automobile paint is more durable than ordinary paint for garden furniture. Consider whether or not you wish to use paint at all in any part of the garden.

## Plant Choice Is Important

Don't plant messy trees.

Choose shrubs that hold their shape and require only light pruning and shaping.

If you are in a dry area and irrigation is a problem, plant as much drought-resistant material as you can.

Avoid plants that are notoriously subject to disease or pests in your area and that require regular spraying.

Remember that vigorous plants are much more disease-resistant than puny ones; favorable growing conditions are the best insurance for a healthy garden.

## Watering

When you water, water thoroughly; don't just sprinkle the surface of the ground. A light sprinkling in the evening is common practice, but all it usually does is create a comfortable climate for various kinds of fungus. The watering needs of his plants is something that every gardener must learn for himself. In rather damp, shady city gardens, for instance, the soil may never look really dry and yet the plants benefit enormously by liberal potations of water. Experience teaches which plants respond best to watering and which suffer most from lack of it.

For roses, shrubs and trees, the best way to water is to let the hose flow very gently for several hours, moving it every once in a while so as to get an even spread of water. By resting the mouth of the hose on a stone, the water can be made to flow more evenly over the surface than if the hose is digging into the ground. In arid areas, depress the beds a few inches to prevent loss of water. Buy a hose of adequate length, a good sprinkler, and, for hand watering, a good nozzle.

When there is a lot of soot or dust, wash down the foliage of plants with a good jet of water. This is especially important for needle-leaf evergreens, to prevent the plant's breathing apparatus from becoming clogged. Watering foliage also helps to keep it free of aphids.

When planting shrubs and trees, deluge them with water at the time of planting, and water frequently in hot weather until they show signs of taking hold. Bare-root material that has been shipped from a distance can usually be put in much better shape for planting by soaking it overnight in a pail or tub of water.

## Tools and Equipment

Spend a little extra to buy good quality tools—trowels that don't bend; digging forks and shovels that don't come apart; pruning shears that cut cleanly, and so on.

Keep equipment in good condition, so that it is always ready for use. Don't leave it outdoors to rust and deteriorate and never put it away dirty.

Wash flower pots before storing them.

## Mulch

Mulching conserves moisture and is an enemy of weeds. Peat moss and buckwheat hulls are excellent mulches in small gardens.

Christmas trees make wonderful winter protection, and, as they decay, good mulch. Their fragrance lasts well into the summer and is especially welcome in city gardens. Pine needles are neutral; spruce and fir are acid and valuable around acid-loving plants.

## Sanitation

The publication in 1962 of Rachel Carson's *The Silent Spring* has focussed attention on the reckless and irresponsible use of chemical sprays without proper consideration of the harm they may cause. Thoughtful people, observing with dismay the disappearance of fish and birds and butterflies from haunts where they were once plentiful, have been troubled for a long time. It is extremely encouraging, therefore, that this enormously complex subject is being debated and explored by those who have power to safeguard health.

It would be unfortunate, however, if every home gardener became gripped with panic and started throwing his spraying and dusting equipment out the window. He would be wiser to remember the principle of moderation, and to familiarize himself with insects that are beneficial so that he does not unwittingly destroy them. Of these, the classic example is the lady bug, lady beetle, or lady bird, as it is variously known. One or another genus of this almost spherical little creature, not bigger than a quarter of an inch long, and colored red or tan with black spots, performs its valuable work in many parts of the world. It is the arch enemy of aphids, preying upon them in both the larval and mature forms. As a child I was taught that it "milked" the aphids, and indeed the literal translation of the Russian word for lady bug is "little cow." The following advice should be read against the background of the above remarks:

Don't wait until a disease or pest has got a good hold before attacking it. Have a good spray pump always in readiness, and a supply of spraying or dusting material always on hand. Hundreds of preparations are available from garden supply dealers, with instructions for use printed clearly on the containers. Many are prepared especially for small garden use and contain multiple-purpose ingredients, so that it is no longer necessary to use one kind of spray for a sucking insect, another for a chewing insect, another for a fungus disease, and so on. Follow the directions exactly, and never exceed the strength recommended. Empty, wash and drain the pump after use.

Never break off a disease- or insect-infested leaf and throw it on the ground. Take a paper sack, drop the offending leaves or blooms into it, twist the top of the sack tightly, and burn it or put it in the trash can. Regular hand-picking can save a lot of spraying with very little effort in a small garden. Aphids on one or two shoots can be crushed and wiped off with the thumb and forefinger.

Keep dead wood cut out of shrubs and trees. If a large surface is exposed, paint it with a wound dressing paint. Small cans of only a few ounces are available at garden supply stores.

## Chapter XI

# *ACTUAL PLANS*

## For a Garden in Texas

Tall, slender trees make a background and frame for the one-story pinkish brick house for which the entrance (Figure 40) was designed. The street is in a residential area, with highly manicured properties on both sides, and the curving expanded metal screen is an ingenious device to give privacy to the porch immediately adjacent to the front door. It also makes a backing for the pool facing the door. Though the screen is highly functional, its light, airy character, combined with a pattern of vines, produces an effect that, both indoors and out, is ornamental.

Mr. Zachariah says: "The ground covers are contained by 1″ x 4″ redwood timbers anchored by 1″ x 3″ x 18″ redwood stakes. The retainers are 2″ above grade. Soaking in water will help to get the proper curves for the redwood.

"The pea gravel ground cover is loose gravel. The boulders are functional as steppingstones. It would be nice to have small clumps of liriope (lily turf) nestled against the boulders. The white crushed marble is roofing material.

"The expanded metal screen is painted first with a rust preventive, then painted any color to fit the scheme of the house. It fits under the eaves of the house and curves downward to a height of 4″, at which point it picks up the elevation of the brick rowlock (4″), which returns to the porch (not indicated) to keep the soil from spilling onto the walk and to give drainage to the shrub bed.

"The pool is also bordered with brick rowlock 4″ high, and there is a single jet spray 2′ high to the rear of the pool. A highly decorative ceiling porch lamp salvaged from an old mansion that had been recently demolished was inverted and placed on a concrete base behind the jet spray in the shrub

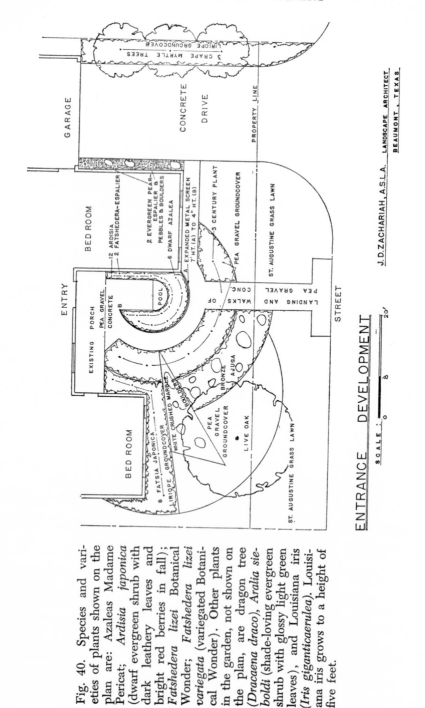

ENTRANCE DEVELOPMENT

SCALE : 0 ... 8 ... 20'

J. D. ZACHARIAH, A.S.L.A.  LANDSCAPE ARCHITECT
BEAUMONT, TEXAS

Fig. 40. Species and varieties of plants shown on the plan are: Azaleas Madame Pericat; *Ardisia japonica* (dwarf evergreen shrub with dark leathery leaves and bright red berries in fall); *Fatshedera lizei* Botanical Wonder; *Fatshedera lizei variegata* (variegated Botanical Wonder). Other plants in the garden, not shown on the plan, are dragon tree (*Dracaena draco*), *Aralia sieboldi* (shade-loving evergreen shrub with glossy light green leaves), and Louisiana iris (*Iris giganticaerulea*). Louisiana iris grows to a height of five feet.

bed. There is a stand pipe drain opening in the curb on the street. The pool is 14″ deep, with a single dwarf potted water-lily near the front. Goldfish if you like.

"The expanded metal may be changed for woven reed (small bamboo) or transparent plastic sheets (preferably with leaves and butterflies), but not the heavy corrugated kind. It must be flexible enough to bend, it must be lightweight in texture, and it must not create a confined or dark area.

"Vines may be used on the expanded metal screen. The vine should be evergreen, such as the Confederate jasmine *(Trachelo-spermum jasminoides)*, which is fragrant, hardy, and small-leafed. The evergreen pear *(Pyrus kawakami)* is dwarf, so as not to interfere with the foundation of the building. It is secured by tying to masonry nails driven directly into the mortar be-tween the bricks; there is no framework. The evergreen pear (popular in landscape work in California) must have sunlight, preferably full sun. It has glossy evergreen foliage and, in Janu-ary, white flowers. The flowers are followed by small inedible fruits.

"The crape-myrtles must be trees, not shrubs, of either single or multiple standard, with open space below and between. The effect is similar to that produced by small birch trees.

"Monkey grass *(Ophiopogon japonicum)* may be substituted for liriope. (Monkey grass is sometimes called mondo and dwarf lily-turf. It is hardier than liriope, which is also known as lily-turf.)

"This plan was exhibited at the National Council Landscape Design School in Little Rock, Arkansas, where I was an in-structor."

### An Architect's Garden in Michigan

Huge elms and a maple abut on the property line of this garden (Figure 41), two blocks from the center of Birming-ham, Michigan, and overlooking the wooded ravine of the Rouge River. A pair of maples in the twelve-foot wide space between the sidewalk and the white two-story house at once push the house back and frame it. There are houses on three sides, but the trees contain the garden, creating a mood as well as a screen. This garden is an excellent illustration of the dif-

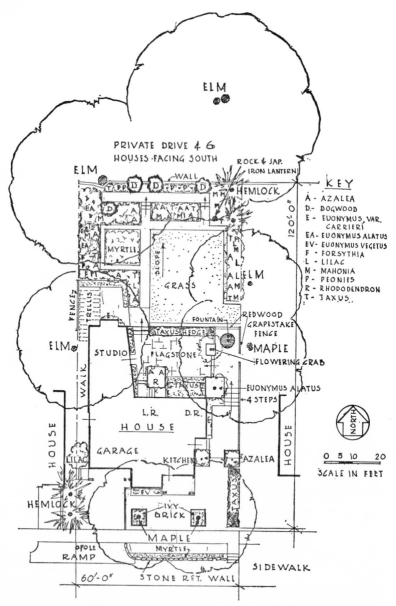

Fig. 41. Architect's garden. Design by Owen A. Luckenbach, A.I.A., and Carl Luckenbach, Designer. Planting by Harry and Beulah Klein, Landscape Architects.

ference between the walled-off privacy obtained by an artificial structure of wood and masonry and the more subtle feeling of seclusion bestowed by forest-size trees.

The garden itself is tightly organized, with a wealth of interest from carefully thought-out detail. Changes in elevation emphasize individual features, such as the small pool and fountain at the end of the corridor leading from the front yard. There is a left turn in front of the pool and a short descent (two steps) to the 28′ x 14′ flagstone terrace. The terrace, screened by a taxus hedge and lighted for night use, is an intimate outdoor living room and the heart of the design; it is a logical extension of the studio and indoor living room and a transition to the paved area adjoining the trellis, the 32′ x 28′ sloping lawn, and the rich shrub plantings which build up to the dogwoods, peonies and hemlock against the rear wall.

In describing this garden, Mr. Luckenbach says: "Our basic aim was to provide a pleasant environment with a minimum of maintenance. All beds are either in redwood boxes or bordered by brick. This gives a strong sense of order in winter and when the beds are not too well maintained. The taxus hedge in front of the flagstone terrace gives complete privacy for entertaining. The pool, with its jet of water, was put in primarily for the sound of water.

"The shades and textures of green in a rhythmic pattern are interesting even when there is little bloom. Since our property is in partial or heavy shade nearly all the time, the only material put in each year are begonias, coleus, impatiens, and tulips and other bulbs."

## A Garden in Los Angeles, California

In the 32′ x 35′ rear yard shown in Figure 42, the original paving was continued in a curving design to form the floor of a shelter with a Fiberglas roof (Plate 9). The fence is high, because a low fence would emphasize the height of the house next door; it is dark, because a white fence, by defining a boundary sharply, can accentuate smallness.

This is a low maintenance garden, with a maximum of paving, and colored rock and pea gravel for ground covers. A *Pittosporum tobira* gives privacy on the East and meets the jas-

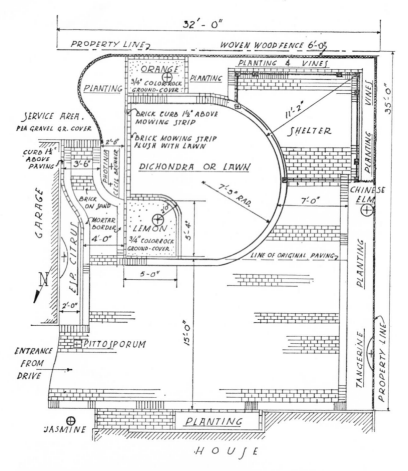

Fig. 42.   Design by John Eyerman, Landscape Architect, for Mr. and Mrs. Albert Drasdo. See also Plate 9.

mine to form an arch over the entrance from the drive. The jasmine (*Jasminum officinale*) has been trained into tree shape and is groomed constantly. The flowers of the jasmine and three kinds of citrus bring fragrance to the garden.

## A Garden in Brooklyn, New York

Though the garden in Figures 43 and 44 is in an urban area, with neighbors' properties on three sides, Mrs. Bauman has achieved an atmosphere of almost woodland seclusion. Redbuds (*Cercis*), an informal hedge of double-file viburnum, and a low wooden wall as part of the deck structure tie into existing boundary hedges and a neighbor's garage wall. Tanbark paving contributes to the woodland feeling; its color harmonizes with the brown wood of the deck and sets off the used-brick floor of the dining area. In spring, clouds of white petals falling on the dark paving from the blossoms of two ancient pear trees give a lightness to the whole area.

The key to the design is the pear trees, one at each end of a diagonal axis. Emphasizing this axis not only increases the apparent length of the garden, but gives each tree its full value in the design. The tree near the tool shed is a frame to the approach from the front yard and a focal point from the dining area. The tree in the dining area, at the other end of the axis, draws one into the garden.

The diagonal axis is repeated in the angle of the steps descending from the deck, again increasing the apparent size of the area but this time in a different direction. Here a Japanese flowering crabapple *(Malus scheideckeri)* focuses the eye. The line of the brick dining area strengthens the diagonal of this axis.

An unusual small hybrid horsechestnut *(Aesculus)* next to the house wall, a pyracantha against the garage wall, and an everblooming mock orange near the dining room area are grown as informal espaliers, each pruned to meet the individual situation. These provide lush greenery without the sacrifice of valuable ground space. The fragrance of the mock orange brings the garden into the house.

Variety in planting gives richness to the garden, but so skillfully have the plants been selected that each takes its place without intrusion in the unified whole. This type of planting, in which there is a slow unfolding of interest, is a valuable device to produce an illusion of spaciousness in a small area. A careful study of the planting plan is a rewarding exercise in how to achieve both harmony and diversity.

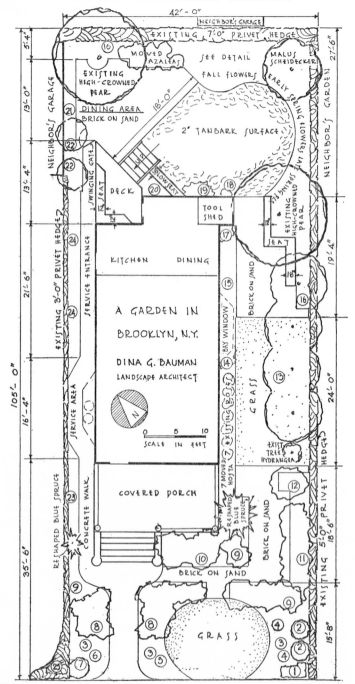

Fig. 43. Brooklyn garden. Design by Dina G. Bauman, Landscape Architect, for Mr. and Mrs. Philip Gordis. See also Plates 10, 11 and 12.

Key to Planting for Fig. 43 (Quantities of shrubs in parentheses):

1. *Pieris floribunda* (3)
2. *Enkianthus campanulatus* (2)
3. Christmas ferns interspersed with
4. *Scilla nutans*
3. Christmas ferns interspersed with
5. *Muscari botryoides*
3. Christmas ferns interspersed with
6. *Chionodoxa luciliae*
7. *Lonicera fragrantissima* (1)
8. *Ilex crenata convexa* (8)
9. *Rhododendron* Boule de Neige (5)
10. *Ilex crenata microphylla* (2)
11. *Viburnum tomentosum* (3)
12. *Aesculus pavia* (1)
13. *Cercis canadensis* (4)
14. *Elaeagnus angustifolia* (1)
15. *Hemerocallis* in variety (Dido, Flava, Gratia, Hyperion, Morocco Red)
16. *Ajuga genevensis*
17. *Philadelphus virginalis* (1)
18. Climbing rose Blaze (1)
19. *Cotoneaster Henryana* (1)
20. *Aesculus* hybrid, trained as informal espalier (1)
21. *Pyracantha coccinea lalandi* (2)
22. *Cornus florida* (2)
23. *Vinca minor*, Bowles, with
24. Daffodils (naturalizing mixture)
25. *Ligustrum ovalifolium* (11)

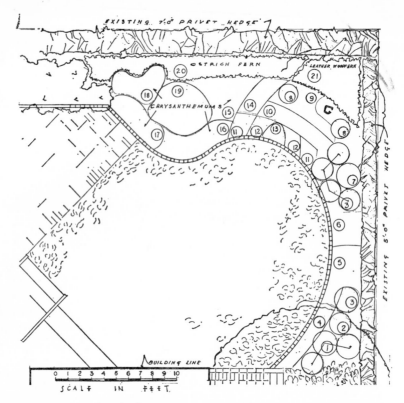

Fig. 44. A detail of a garden in Brooklyn, New York (see also Fig. 43).

### Key to Flowers and Ferns

1. Red peonies
2. White oriental poppy
3. White peonies
4. Dark blue iris
5. White iris
6. Light blue iris
7. Red oriental poppy
8. Bleeding heart
9. White trillium
10. Red coral bells
11. White candytuft
12. Pale yellow alyssum
13. Blue veronica
14. Columbine
15. Chrysanthemum, Ivory Spoon
16. Chrysanthemum, Cushion Apricot
17. Chrysanthemum, Cushion White
18. Chrysanthemum, Yellow Spoon
19. Chrysanthemum, Bronze-gold Spoon
20. Ostrich Fern
21. Leather Woodfern

## A Pie-shaped Lot

Figures 45 and 46 are before-and-after plans of a garden in Birmingham, Michigan. The designer and co-owner is Mrs. Beulah H. Klein, Landscape Architect. The construction and planting were done under her close supervision.

In the original design, the garage literally cut the space to the rear of the house in half and the neighbor's house was the focal point as one entered the drive. The flower garden beyond the garage, besides lacking privacy, seemed to float off into the adjoining property.

Relocation of the garage brings this unrelated area into the garden, increases the size of the living area, walls off the neighbor's house, and at the same time complies with the zoning laws as to location of buildings. The design of the driveway is such that one car may be driven in or out of the garage while the second car is parked to the right of the garage entrance.

In front of the house, the porch has been tied to the building by removing the top-heavy evergreen planting in front of it, and by planting and paving at each side. Regrading, and the construction of a brick walk with two pairs of steps to replace an informal sloping path, dignifies the pedestrian approach to the house. Brick paving carries through to the rear and contributes to the pattern of the garden and its charm. Since the house is white, the red brick has a warming effect in winter.

The picket fence from the former flower garden behind the garage now runs along the right property line. To the left and rear heavy planting screens the garden from outsiders. Mrs. Klein writes: "It takes frequent pruning to keep things in scale, but we are glad to do that for privacy."

The plant material includes: four varieties of taxus, Japanese cutleaf maples, flowering crabapples, bayberry, forsythia, *Viburnum tomentosum* and *V. setigera, Azalea mollis*, mahonia, *Cotoneaster apiculata*, lilacs, Alpine currant, red barberry, *Magnolia stellata*, Moraine locust, pyracantha, hemlock. Ground covers are myrtle *(Vinca minor)* and pachysandra. *Bergenia cordifolia, Hosta grandiflora alba*, lilies, chrysanthemums and peonies are among the perennials. The only annuals used are zinnias, salvia Blue Bedder, dwarf lemon marigolds and Riverside ageratum. Bulbs are daffodils and tulips.

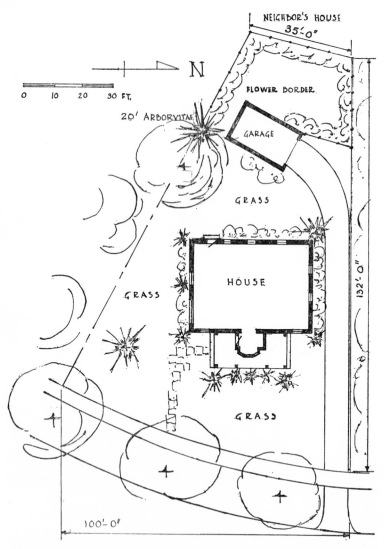

Fig. 45. Pie-shaped lot. "Before" plan of a garden in Birmingham, Michigan.

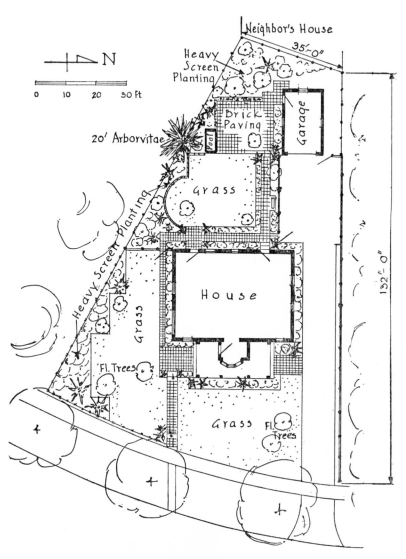

Fig. 46. "After" plan of garden shown in Fig. 45. Design by
Beulah H. Klein, Landscape Architect.

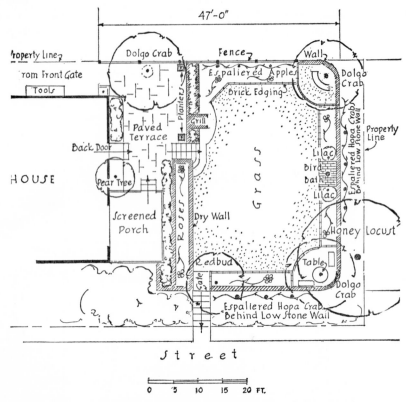

Fig. 47.  Iowa garden. Design by Elizabeth Howerton, Landscape Architect for Mrs. John Sebelein. See also Plates 13 and 14.

## A Two-Level Garden in Iowa

Crabapples espaliered above a wall of rough stone bring a breath of New England orchards into this charming and livable little garden in Davenport, Iowa. In early May their fragrant flowers are billowing clouds; in summer the foliage is a screen from neighboring properties and a green backing for flower beds; in winter the horizontal lines of the branches provide a strong and attractive frame. The white-flowered Dolgo crab and the rose pink Hopa are dual-purpose varieties, flowering profusely in spring and later producing fruit that makes excellent jelly.

This is a do-it-yourself garden; the owners trained the espaliered trees from one-inch whips, laid the brick edging which give crispness to the design, and built the garden benches to conform to the small size of the garden.

Note, in the design, the use of the bird bath and the lilacs to build up a focal point as one descends the steps from the terrace, and the way in which the lower steps are turned towards the gate opening onto the street. Note, also, the two slightly raised grass sitting areas, one under the honey locust and the other at the opposite end of the garden under a Dolgo crab. Increased height in the wall behind these areas strengthens the corners of the garden and adds interest. The broad, rounded leaves of the redbud *(Cercis canadensis),* and the lacy foliage of the honey locust *(Gleditsia triacanthos)* make a pleasing contrast to the foliage of the flowering crabs.

## A Garden Twelve Feet Wide

The narrow garden in Figure 48 was designed for a house on a tree-lined street in an old residential section of Brooklyn, New York. It is one of a row of similar houses, and the gardens make a series of rectangles, each as wide as the house to which it is attached. The only entrance to this garden is through the kitchen, which is on the level of the summer breakfast nook. The rest of the area is roughly on the level of the second floor of the house. The garden is shaded at the far end and at one side from trees and large shrubs in neighbors' gardens.

Since major reconstruction was not practicable, the design retains the original terrace and paved area next to the kitchen. Otherwise, a spiral flight of iron stairs could have been built from the dining room on the second floor to the garden, and the area of the existing terrace excavated. This would have permitted a large outdoor living room, with graceful steps ascending to the planted area.

Vertical boards in the fence are preferred to horizontal boards, which would emphasize the length of the garden. Another device to shorten the yard is the circular paved area, with a piece of sculpture in the middle, placed about two-thirds of the distance from the terrace to the back fence. A banking of shrubs behind the seat helps to push this forward.

The original garden contained four iron posts for laundry lines. These were so typical of little backyard city lots in New York two and more generations ago that they are practically a period feature. Few remain, but when they do, especially if

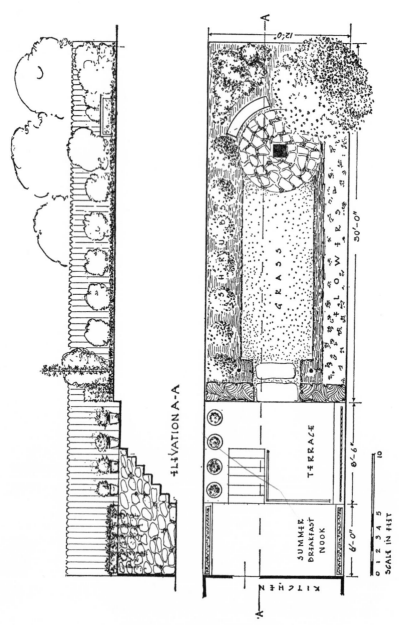

Fig. 48.   A garden 12' wide.

they are of wood with an ornamental carved top, they can often be worked into a design as supports for pillar roses or other climbers. Two were kept in this yard, just behind the clipped hedge at the entrance to the planted area, where they provide a useful vertical accent.

The planting is extremely simple. Boxes on the narrow ledge above the breakfast nook contain ivy which drapes the upper part of the wall. Potted plants are colorful on one side of the terrace; on the other side a vine on a trellis screens the sitting area. A quick-growing annual vine is suitable here, since there isn't room for a heavy woody vine, and if a climbing rose is not kept tied and trimmed its errant prickly shoots are a nuisance. Clematis is brittle and might be broken. English ivy, of course, could be trained in an interesting pattern and would provide year-round interest.

*Ilex crenata,* or an upright form of yew *(Taxus)* would make the most pleasing hedge; the hedge should be evergreen if possible and thorny material should be avoided. Two objections to yew in this particular garden are that the soil is very acid and the area is too exposed to city soot to be ideal for any needle-leaf plant.

A nice, medium-sized *Euonymus alatus* was growing just behind the hedge; it was retained and is colorful in fall. Another suitable shrub for this location would be *Abelia grandiflora.*

There are several reasons, practical and aesthetic, for planting one side of the garden to shrubs and the other to flowers: 1. The side where the shrubs are is shady. 2. The soil is acid and it is simpler to segregate a collection of acid-loving shrubs and add lime to the entire flower bed. 3. It is a little more interesting to have this imbalance.

The shrubs should be rather low and spaced so that they will not become too solid; if they are high and tightly jammed there will be a feeling of crowding in this small space. Slow-growing boxwood would be wonderful; a dwarf form of *Ilex crenata convexa* or *bullata* would be a good substitute. The five low shrubs should be all of one kind; a mixed assortment would tend to produce spottiness. The under-planting is the shade-loving pachysandra; its light green is a better contrast to *Ilex crenata* and boxwood than ivy would be. Pachysandra is also planted as an evergreen border to the flower bed; it will be invasive but is not difficult to control. Its use on both sides of the garden has a unifying effect.

The shrub next to the seat should be somewhat larger than the main shrub planting, and of a different texture; *Pieris japonica* or one of the coarser-leafed varieties of *Ilex crenata* would be suitable. The planting behind the seat should be heavy and quite high; *Rhododendron maximum* would be splendid.

The area is so small that the tree might very well be a large shrub, but not a type that produces multiple stems from the base. A fine old hawthorn or dogwood would be handsome; if the climate were mild enough a crape-myrtle (*Lagerstroemia indica*) would be perfect. Whatever the tree or shrub, its top should spread rather loosely; it should not be a tight, rounded tree.

There is just enough sun in this garden to have a panel of grass in the center; if grass were not possible this would be a place for a carefully worked out design in brick. In sun, varieties of creeping thyme would be very pretty between the stones in the circular paved area. *Arenaria verna caespitosa,* a moss-like plant, can be used in both sun and shade.

The flower bed should provide some color all season.

## Square Gardens

The design shown in Figures 49, 50 and 52 illustrates the use of a diagonal axis to produce an illusion of length in a square area. The design could be developed at almost any scale, either for an entire garden, or for a small specialty garden within a larger area. Small units devoted primarily to one type of plant, such as roses or herbs or chrysanthemums or azaleas or even annuals are often very satisfactory, not only to indulge a hobbyist's interest in a particular plant, but to provide a degree of separateness for those who prefer several small areas to relax in rather than one generalized area. Sometimes the shape of a lot dictates this kind of treatment.

Whatever type of garden is chosen, the central area should be kept open and either paved or planted with grass or a grass substitute: if it were smothered with flowers the feeling of design would be lost. Depressing it a few inches adds interest,

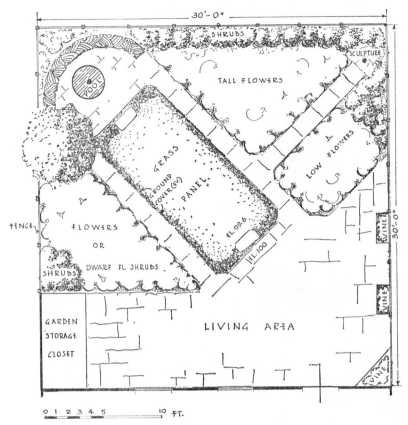

Fig. 49. A square garden designed for flowers.

and planting the low bank formed at the sides and ends with an evergreen ground cover strengthens the axis. Wintercreeper (*Euonymus fortunei vegetus*) or ivy (*Hedera helix*) are excellent plants for this purpose. The varieties of ivy known as 238th Street and Baltic are especially good, since both are somewhat smaller leafed than typical English ivy and would hug the ground more closely. Where *Vinca minor* (periwinkle) is evergreen, it makes a delightful shiny covering and the little lavender flowers are pretty in spring. Small bulbs such as crocus, scilla, chionodoxa, fritillaria and grape hyacinths near the steppingstones at the entrance to the lawn would make a tapestry in spring and could be followed in fall by meadow saffron or autumn crocus (*Colchicum* and *Crocus* species).

VARIETY IN PAVING.   Some variety in the paving might be intro-

duced by using brick near the hedge and flagstone for the rest
of the paving, or vice versa. Water, even if the pool is not much
bigger than a large bowl, is appealing to many and can be
treated in a number of ways. A coarse pebbly texture on the
floor of a small pool is much more interesting than a plain surface; small ceramic tiles of the kind imported from Italy are
beautiful and their use is a challenge to a person interested in
crafts. No pool is too small for a pygmy water lily. In gardens
where winter color must be introduced artificially, colored tile
on the coping of a pool or in other stonework can be a very
pleasing note.

THE HEDGE. The hedge behind the pool should be clipped
evergreen not less than three or four feet high for a garden of
the scale shown. In the North, an upright variety of yew
(*Taxus*) such as the varieties *capitata* or Hicks, or *Ilex crenata,*
can be used. In somewhat milder areas boxwood (*Buxus*) would
provide one of the most beautiful hedges it is possible to have.
In really warm sections, where evergreen material is more common than deciduous, the choice is wide: pittosporum and
myrtle (*Myrtus communis*) are two examples. In most parts of
the country English ivy trained over a support of galvanized
wire mesh makes a good solid hedge.

These recommendations apply to any one of the types of garden mentioned. Now let us consider the design for a general
planting, and for various kinds of specialized planting.

A FLOWER GARDEN, FIGURE 49

*The tree.* A high-crowned, slender tree, with a trunk branching some feet from the ground, is called for; a multiple-trunked
spreading tree would encroach altogether too much on a small
space, besides looking chunky and, by its squatness, emphasizing the squareness of the area. If anything has to be sacrificed
to the budget, it should not be the tree; a good-sized shapely
specimen will immediately establish the character of this little
area; it should be the pièce de résistance around which the rest
of the planting revolves.

The difficulty about suggesting alternatives is that certain
plants go together aesthetically and others do not, and if a number of choices are offered there is a danger that the wrong kinds
will find themselves side by side and the planting will lack sen-

sitivity: an analogy would be mixing satin brocade and striped denim in a room. There are really no set rules about the juxtaposition of plants, and unlikely material can sometimes be mixed with immense effect; it is also true that tastes differ a great deal and much depends on the individual situation. For these reasons, I am always unhappy about plant lists and offer the following suggestions with a bow to the judgment of the gardener on the spot.

For an evergreen tree in this garden, I cannot think of anything more effective than a mature Scotch pine *(Pinus sylvestris),* with its wonderful orange bark and rather short bluish needles. The lower branches of the Scotch pine tend to die, and by a mature specimen I mean one from which the lower branches have been removed. An evergreen heavily branched to the ground is not suitable at all.

If a deciduous tree is preferred, the silk tree *(Albizzia julibrissin),* with its dome-shaped crown and pretty feathery foliage, is a good choice in the North. A variety of honey locust *(Gleditsia triacanthos),* such as Shadesmaster or Imperial, and the goldenrain tree *(Koelreuteria paniculata)* are other possibilities. A fine old pear tree would be beautiful. In the far South, this would be a splendid location for a jacaranda, with its incised foliage and showy blue flowers. In warm areas, certain species of acacia would be attractive.

*Shrubs.* If the area is enclosed with a high fence or wall, the rear boundary, opposite the living area, would be a splendid place to espalier the red- or orange-berried pyracantha, given enough sun to induce flowering and fruiting. This would also be a place to espalier forsythia or mock orange; treated thus these shrubs would become a simple background when flowering was finished and would not intrude the uninteresting bulk of unrestrained specimens. They would, however, contribute nothing in winter. For a year-round green wall, yew could be espaliered. Ivy could be grown as a solid covering, or trained in vertical panels on trellis work or galvanized wire mesh. A row of background shrubs could, of course, be grown informally, but they would cut down the planting area in front and, unless carefully chosen, might make the garden look crowded.

The shrub or shrubs to the right of the bed labeled low flow-

ers should be chosen for year-round character. A combination
of *Pieris japonica* and *Enkianthus campanulatus* would be
ideal. Both belong to the family Ericaceae and are acid-loving.
Pieris is evergreen; enkianthus is not, but it has an extremely
interesting growth habit and splendid fall color and makes a
good minor contrast to pieris.

In warm sections camellias or gardenias would be beautiful
here, and in intermediate climates a great mound of boxwood;
there is room for its billowing form to assert itself.

In the triangular bed on the left, the shrub or shrubs next to
the garden storage closet should also be strong in character and
not an indeterminate mass. Rhododendron would be good, and
in cold climates should be selected for a variety that does not
droop dismally when the thermometer falls below freezing. A
large-leafed holly would be magnificent, and, in California,
English laurel *(Prunus laurocerasus)*. Whatever shrub is chosen,
it should provide a screen for the storage closet and a pleasing
background for the plants in front of it. This shrub, and the
group at the other side of the lot, will frame the garden as seen
from the pool.

*Vines.*   In choosing vines, study the character of the house, its
height, and the color and texture of the walls. The chapter on
vines will provide a clue. Vines may be grown either in pockets
in the paving, or in large planters. Before deciding to make
pockets in the paving, especially when it is close to the house,
consider whether the roots will become so vigorous, and the
stems so trunk-like, that the paving will be forced up or underground structures affected. With an old house, there is sometimes real danger of introducing moisture into the cellar if paving is removed next to a wall.

*Flowers.*   The above planting establishes the backbone of the
garden; flowers are a more frivolous choice, since it is easier to
change their scheme. A tentative suggestion is a big clump of
evergreen daylilies in the corner of the triangle next to the
hedge, and another near the sculpture. Tall perennials such as
phlox, delphiniums and lilies, would be lovely at the back of
the bed, with lower-growing kinds towards the front. Coral
bells *(Heuchera)* and columbine *(Aquilegia)* make delightful
foreground plants.

An edging of a very dwarf form of boxwood or *Ilex crenata* in all the flower beds would contribute much to the winter form of the garden.

*Bulbs and Annuals.*  The bed marked low flowers would be excellent for bulbs, followed by a low-growing massed annual, such as petunia, verbena, or *Phlox drummondi,* or for a bedding plant such as begonia. A uniform planting is suggested for this bed, rather than a lot of little spots. Fragrant plants, such as petunias and heliotrope, would be especially pleasing so close to the house. In winter, this bed would be a splendid place for a Christmas tree; in the cold outdoors it would retain its freshness for many weeks.

*A Rose Bed.*  The triangle on the left, since it runs back from the living area to the tree, calls for some gradation of treatment, with more thought for detail near the terrace and higher-growing bulkier material at the far end. This would make a very nice rose bed, with strong-growing varieties towards the back, and daintier, less vigorous varieties near the walk and the terrace. The section on roses contains descriptions of suitable varieties.

A HERB GARDEN, FIGURE 50

Figure 50 develops the design as a herb garden. A complete list of all the plants it would be possible to grow in this area would crowd the plan; a selection has been chosen for height, texture, color, culinary usefulness, and historical or sentimental interest.

The triangle near the storage closet is treated as a lightly shaded area, with bee balm *(Monarda)* to give a spot of bright color (shades of red and pink) near the apple tree; a collection of mints, with their varying textures, colors and flavors (woolly, curly, peppermint, and so on); a plot of sweet-scented geraniums, for their delicious fragrance and ornamental, often velvety leaves; a clump of pale primroses next to the terrace, and, in the background, the light green freshness of elderberry. An improved variety of elderberry, known as Adams, is now available commercially, so it is not necessary to collect a plant from the wilds.

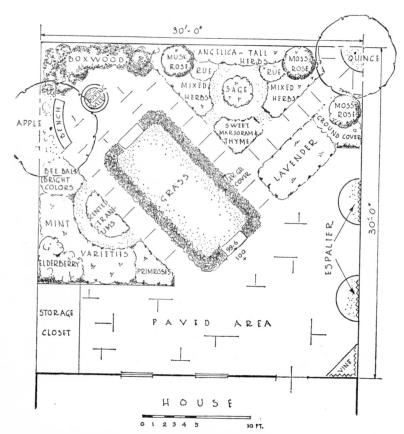

Fig. 50.  A square garden designed for herbs.

The musk rose near the fence could be Pax, a highly per-
fumed everblooming variety with rather large, semi-double
ivory flowers; or Kathleen, the apple-blossom rose, single, white
when open, shell pink in bud. Both reach fence height and
more, or can be pruned as shrubs. A red moss is suggested for
the distant variety, and a pink next to the bed of lavender.

Angelica is a tall, rigid-stemmed biennial or perennial (keep
the flowers cut to make it perennial) that will make a good
background for the lower planting in front. The rue will make
two lovely mounds of blue green and produce a profusion of
canary-yellow flowers in spring. Its foliage will persist long
after the early frosts. It is a woody perennial and valuable in
difficult gardens for its hardy constitution. It should be pruned
hard in early spring to prevent its getting leggy.

*Photograph by Gottscho-Schleisner, Inc.*

Plate 15.   In small, enclosed gardens in heavily-settled areas a
feeling of greater space and interest can often be achieved by
breaking up the area. Here a niche at the end of a walk suggests
an intimate place to sit. The wings of the niche, adorned with
clinging plants, frame the figure and enlarge the planting possibilities.

*Mary Deputy Cattell, Landscape Architect; photographs by Gottscho-Schleisner, Inc.*

Plate 16, opposite:   A high brick boundary wall with flagstone cap is lightened by an openwork pattern. Note the Chinese Chippendale design of the fence and the well-proportioned posts and finials. Note also repetition of the fence design in the gate. This is another small garden whose beauty is enhanced by a single large tree.

Plate 17.   A detail in the same garden, showing the deft pattern of the cut flagstone paving. This view brings out the handsome frieze effect of the openwork brick and the finish given by the flagstone cap. Pansies are interplanted with the tulips. The ornamental container to the left is of lead, an eminently satisfying material in this type of garden.

*Robert Zion and Harold Breen, Site Planners and Landscape Architects,*
*New York, N. Y.; photograph by Alexandre Georges*

Plate 18. A raised entrance garden, with evergreens (pachysandra, *Vinca minor*, boxwood) for year-round interest and low
maintenance. Spring color is from bulbs, summer color from pots of
pink and white geraniums. The big elm growing at the original level
has been walled; lighting in the well sharpens its effect at night.
The obvious contribution of the tree to the design is an answer to
those who worry about a large tree in a small space.

The rough gray texture of garden sage, with its spikes of lavender-colored flowers, is suggested for the little round bed in the center of this triangle. It is ornamental, extremely hardy, and a staple in seasoning. Thyme and sweet marjoram, also valuable culinary herbs, are finer leafed and will be pretty against the background of sage. There is room for more than one variety of thyme.

The mixed herbs should include the lettuce-green sweet basil, decorative as well as excellent in salads, French tarragon, summer savory and pot marjoram. Clumps of chives may also be planted here. A number of variations in this brief list are possible.

For a ground cover under the pink moss rose next to the terrace, gill-over-the-ground *(Nepeta hederacea)* is suitable.

In a mild climate, rosemary is a delightful hedge in a herb garden.

A Persian walnut might take the place of the apple tree, and a medlar could be substituted for the quince. For a description of the medlar, see the chapter on fruit and nut trees.

*Paving.* The warm color of old brick is always pleasing in a herb garden, where it sets off the soft grays and greens of the foliage better than most materials. The narrow paths inside the two triangles are more a means of getting to the plants than walks and would probably be most satisfactory sown to grass or surfaced with tanbark. Steppingstones would also be a solution, but solid paving might tend to make the area too rigid. Also, by using a less permanent surface, it would be easier to change the design.

A KNOT GARDEN

Figure 51 shows a detail of a traditional herb garden, designed for the New York Botanical Garden by The Herb Society of America (see Plate 23).

The centerpiece is a knot garden. Knot gardens of pansies, marigolds, forget-me-nots and other small flowering plants have long ceased to be popular, but knot gardens of low compact herbs of contrasting colors and textures are not uncommon. The space between the twists of the knot is usually surfaced with colored gravel or chipped rock. In this knot garden the three

LEGEND:    GREEN SANTOLINA·
           GRAY SANTOLINA (LAVENDER COTTON)
           DWARF BOXWOOD

Fig. 51. A knot garden.

plants used are gray santolina, known also as lavender cotton (*Santolina chamaecyparissus*), bright green santolina (*Santolina virens*), and dwarf boxwood.

Other perennial herbs suitable for knot gardens are germander (*Teucrium chamaedrys*), the shrubby garden thyme (*Thymus vulgaris*), and a dwarf form of lavender. Parsley and the forms of nasturtium that make compact, rounded plants can be used in a temporary knot.

### A FRUIT AND VEGETABLE GARDEN, FIGURE 52

Figure 52 suggests a simple fruit and vegetable garden. Not everyone is interested in flowers, and there is no reason at all why a kitchen garden should not be ornamental, or why vegetables should not be combined with certain flowers. Annuals are usually the most appropriate and provide season-long color.

A number of vines and shrubs that are commonly grown for ornament produce fruit that is suitable for jellies and preserves. Examples are the Oregon grape (*Mahonia aquifolium*), the black haw (*Viburnum prunifolium*), dwarf Japanese flowering quince (*Chaenomeles japonica*), and varieties of actinidia, a handsome woody vine.

For a tree in this garden, see the chapter on fruit and nut trees.

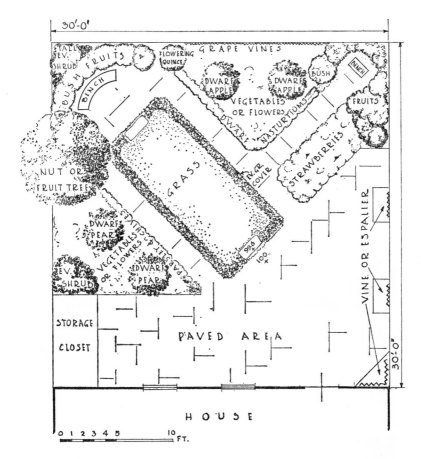

Fig. 52. A square garden designed for fruits and vegetables.

A CIRCLE IN A SQUARE, FIGURE 53

This design for a diagonal-axis garden can also be adapted in a number of ways. It would be especially pretty for roses,

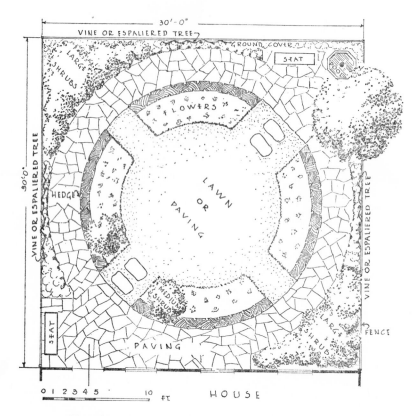

Fig. 53. A circular garden designed in a square.

chrysanthemums or annuals, and could be worked out with different colors in each bed. It could also be a herb garden, or a fragrant garden. It would be effective at a much larger scale.

The shrubs on either side of the entrance to the garden should be chosen for year-round effectiveness, and should be rather low and spreading; yew or boxwood would be a good choice in the North. The hedge should also be of superior quality, and shorn; not too high but high enough to make a background for the flower beds. The shrubs in the corners should be fairly high and full, and rich-looking. The notes on plant material for Figure 49 should be read in connection with this garden.

The paving is the kind sometimes known as "crazy," that is, it consists of irregular-sized pieces of stone. It is the easiest to lay in a circular area and is much improved in appearance if the pockets between the stones are planted. Sandwort *(Arenaria verna caespitosa)*, a moss-like plant, is excellent for this purpose. White thyme *(Thymus serpyllum albus)* is another popular plant for paving stones, and, where the winters are not too severe, the gray woolly thyme *(Thymus serpyllum lanuginosus)* is very pretty.

Interest can be added to this garden by depressing the lawn a few inches.

## Designs for Brownstones

Many stories below the towering cubes that are rapidly changing the character of northeastern cities, there are still blocks of three- and four-story houses, set back a few feet from the street and with an old-fashioned stoop to the "parlor" floor. These solidly built little houses are the last stronghold against wholesale demolition, and if more owners realized the potential charm of their doll-sized front yards, the days of their dwellings might be prolonged. People tend to cling with greater tenacity to land they have cultivated than to that which merely supports bricks and mortar; also, a street of dismal front yards brings a glint to the eye of slum clearance committees.

In New York City houses of this type are commonly called brownstones, though they may very well be of brick. The gardens shown in Figures 54, 55 and 56 were designed for Manhattan, but they could be adapted for gardens in other cities in the Northeast.

## A Brownstone Back Yard

Many thousands of these little yards are hidden behind the older houses of Manhattan, typically enclosed with high board fences and looking from rear windows like a series of open boxes. Occasionally fences are removed to make a community area for several houses, but more often owners prefer privacy. In a vast mechanized city in the space age, these walled-in areas, so secret from the street and personal to the owner, possess a value out of all proportion to their size. In summer the drooping fronds of ailanthus trees help to screen the occupants from the view of upper-floor neighbors.

A New York City back yard normally possesses two distinc-

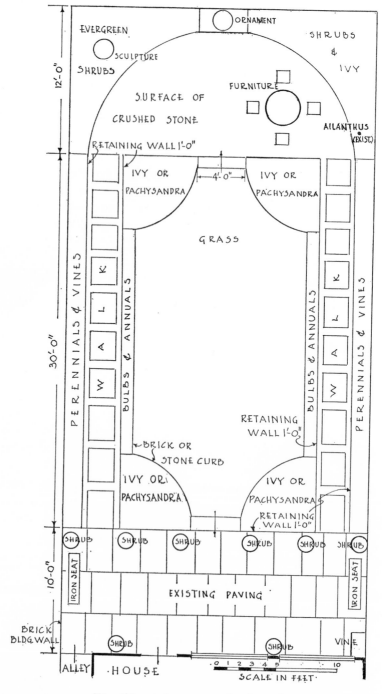

Fig. 54. A brownstone back yard.

tive features—an average of 400 square feet of bluestone paving, and a sub-surface of glacial rocks of many sizes, colors and
textures. In many yards the paving pattern dates from the Victorian era in which it was laid and forms a narrow path round
a central rectangle of planting, with wider paving near the
house.

In the design in Figures 54 and 55 the original paving next
to the house has been retained. It would be more pleasing if the
lines between the rows of flagstone were broken, but it is often
not practicable to move large flagstones four inches thick and
weighing 400 pounds. The stones in the original walks parallel
to the side fences are pushed a little apart, and those from the
old path at the end of the garden are used as a base for the
ornament and to provide steps at the entrance to the lawn. The
remainder are broken to make part of the retaining walls. The
rest of the stone for the retaining walls comes from rocks excavated in the yard.

PLANTS. Two plants of Boston ivy *(Parthenocissus tricuspidata)* will in a very few years cover the brick wall of the
apartment house on the right.

A variety of Japanese holly *(Ilex crenata)* is suggested for the
tubs.

The shrubs at the far end of the garden should be strong-
growing evergreen material, such as rhododendrons *(R. maximum* and *R. catawbiense),* Japanese holly, euonymus and *Pieris
japonica.*

The lattice panels along the fence lend themselves to annual
vines such as morning glories and moonflower, or for a perennial vine such as sweet autumn clematis *(Clematis paniculata),*
which flowers in September. Other kinds of clematis should be
avoided in the highly acid soil and under the difficult conditions of a New York City garden. Forsythia and virginal mock
orange *(Philadelphus virginalis)* would be pretty espaliered
against the lattice panels.

Perennial plants for the raised beds along the fence are:
bearded irises (sun), hostas (shade), daylilies *(Hemerocallis),*
and chrysanthemums. These should be planted between the
vines, with a low-growing floppy annual such as petunias at the
foot of the lattice. The annual clockvine *(Thunbergia),* with

Fig. 55. A brownstone back yard.

soft yellow and white flowers, and the perennial blue plumbago, would both cascade over the edge of the beds.

Tulips and daffodils, planted in clumps rather than a stiff
line, should be used for early spring color. The early flowering
Fosteriana tulip, Red Emperor, cannot be too highly recommended for bringing a city garden to life in mid-April. The
huge flowers are scarlet-vermilion, and when fully opened re-
veal strong black stamens against a violet splotch at the base
of the cup. A good tulip to plant in a clump near Red Emperor
is Orange Wonder, a Mendel tulip, more red than orange,
which in my garden blooms at the end of April just as Red Emperor is fading and prolongs color of a similar intensity for another ten days. By that time the early spring flowering tulips
are opening.

The narrow beds along the edge of the lawn are admirably
adapted for small spring bulbs, followed by low growing annuals such as dwarf marigolds. If desired, the grass may be continued up to the low retaining wall, with spring flowering bulbs
and autumn flowering crocus planted in the grass. Other plants
to grow here are English daisies and violets.

The thymes, so good between steppingstones, are a poor choice
for most city yards of the kind described. Sedums are tough, as
is the mock strawberry (*Duchesnea indica*), and ajuga. Creeping Charlie (*Lysimachia nummularia*) is another possibility. It
should be remembered that plants that normally get out of
hand are so restrained under difficult city conditions that they
acquire a new usefulness.

Evergreen ground covers are ivy and pachysandra.

The initial work of making this garden would be heavy, but
once done it would be extremely easy to maintain and would
always look presentable.

## A Tiny Front Yard

The tiny city yard in Figure 56 is typically enclosed with an
ornate wrought-iron fence, and is further set off with iron window guards, an elaborate iron door under the stoop, and all
kinds of fancy trimming on the stoop banisters. The brownstone
or brick of the building is softly weathered, or painted pink or
white or green or yellow.

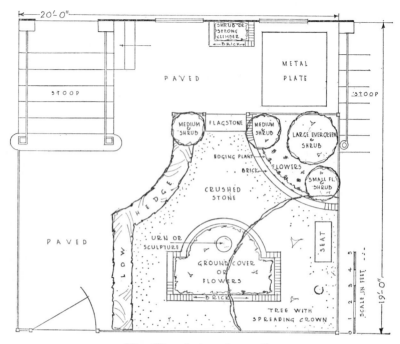

Fig. 56.  A tiny city yard.

Front yards possess the big advantage of free air circulation, which is often badly lacking in city back yards. And if they are on the north side of the street, they usually get full sunlight. The chief threats to these front plots are vandalism and prowling cats, but an aroused gardening public would not dismiss wanton destruction with a shrug and would be more aggressive about the droves of cats abandoned by irresponsible owners and unbelievably destructive in many parts of large cities.

Sample designs for front yards are not very satisfactory, because actual planning involves details determined by such things as the position of metal area plates, leaders, projecting masonry, the color of the house, and features of the house next door. The accompanying plan, however, illustrates several points:

The shrubs are placed to screen the basement windows and the unsightly iron plate, and also to make a backing for the flower bed near the fence. The shrub or strong climber between the window completes the background as seen from the street. By setting the flower bed back a little, it is made less accessible to passers-by. The tree on the right helps to contain the yard as an individual unit. Some may question putting a seat in such a tiny yard, but no matter how small the area, a seat is useful; it is pleasant to sit for a few minutes when one is working, and to have somewhere to put shears or trowel.

A front yard should be planned to be seen from all sides. Plants may be selected from the following list:

I. SUN.

*Climbers:* Wistaria; fleece vine; hardy climbing roses Blaze, Dr. Van Fleet, City of York.

*Shrubs between windows:* Firethorn *(Pyracantha coccinea lalandi)*, espaliered against wall; forsythia espaliered; flowering almond; California privet.

*Shrubs in bed:* Spreading euonymus ( *E. patens,* half-evergreen); *Euonymus radicans vegetus* (glossy, evergreen); wintergreen barberry; glossy abelia (half-evergreen); bridal wreath (deciduous); Japanese flowering quince (*Chaenomeles lagenaria,* deciduous); hardy blue hydrangea (deciduous); shrub rose The Fairy.

*Clipped hedge:* Dwarf Japanese flowering quince *(Chaenomeles japonica);* California privet. Don't plant yew or any other needle leaf evergreen. Japanese holly might be used, but it would be in too exposed a position if dogs or cats were a problem. The plant at the end near the flagstone should be clipped higher, or left unclipped.

*Edging plants:* Dwarf Japanese holly; dwarf boxwood.

*Ground covers:* Periwinkle (myrtle); English ivy (there might be a little winter burning).

*Flowers:* Bulbs, followed by annuals, such as petunias, zinnias, marigolds, ageratum, lantana; or bedding plants such as coleus, begonias.

Petunias reseed themselves vigorously in the city. They revert to a small bright magenta flower, but come back faithfully, in sun and shade, and many a little front plot is brilliant year after year because of a packet of seed someone once scattered.

*Tree:* Moraine locust; goldenrain tree *(Koelreuteria);* silk tree *(Albizzia);* flowering cherry; flowering crab; saucer magnolia. (See section on trees for descriptions.)

II.   SHADE.

*Climbers:*   Wistaria; fleece vine; Boston ivy.

*Shrubs between windows:*   Japanese holly; California privet; spreading euonymus.

*Shrubs in bed:*   Rhododendron; spreading euonymus; Japanese holly; California privet; *Euonymus radicans vegetus;* ivy trained loosely on a frame of wire; blue hydrangea; glossy abelia.

*Clipped hedge:*   California privet.

*Edging plants:*   Pachysandra; dwarf Japanese holly; dwarf boxwood.

*Ground covers:*   Pachysandra; English ivy.

*Flowers:*   Impatiens; tobacco plant.

*Tree:*   Magnolia; Moraine locust; willow; white mulberry.

## A Contemporary Garden

Though the site of the garden in Figure 57 is the south of France, it was designed by an American landscape architect for a client who spends several months a year in America and has developed a liking for American things. Mr. Miceli had not seen the property and his approach to the problem is interesting. He says:

"The building, originally an eighteenth century winery, was remodeled to provide a summer home and future permanent residence for the client. The court was created by demolishing part of the original structure. In the course of remodeling, the huge exposed wooden beams and the old tiled floors of the interior were retained.

"I received my biggest clue to a design concept when the client told me that although the architecture was eighteenth century, a painting of the period seemed out of character but that a Mondrian or a Picasso on its rugged walls looked 'as though born there.' I therefore concluded that a contemporary court, of the style that may be described as Californian, was the solution."

All the other plans in this book are accompanied by planting notes. This is not. (The only information offered the reader is

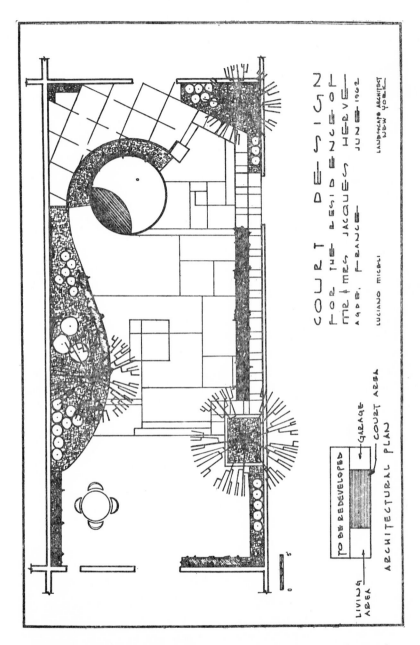

Fig. 57. Contemporary garden. Design by Luciano Miceli, Landscape Architect, New York, N. Y., for Mr. and Mrs. Jacques Herve, Agde, France.

that at the top left there is a table with four chairs and, at the right, a circle which combines a pool and deck.) The plan is presented to the reader as a challenge to visualize the garden purely in terms of form, line, color, space, composition. When a picture has formed in his mind, he should search for the plants in his location that will, for him, best interpret the design.

# PART II

## Chapter I

# PLANTS AND PLANTING

It is estimated that some 32,000 plant varieties, other than native material, are cultivated in the continental United States and Canada. In any one suburban area a huge number is available. And yet the *classes* of plants needed to landscape a property, whatever its size, are very few.

A lot of trouble can be saved if a gardener's first thinking is about classes, not individual plants. For instance, plant material for every purpose is embraced in the following short list:

1. Trees
2. Shrubs
3. Ground covers, including grass
4. Climbing plants
5. Flowers

By the time the gardener has made his plan, he has made his first planting decision, which is, the proportion of the garden to be allotted to each of the above five classes of plants. He is now ready for the next step, which is to select material within each class.

## Choosing Plants

No matter how well a garden has been planned, it can be spoiled if the plants are not aesthetically compatible. On the broad canvas of woods and fields, Nature achieves her own casual rhythm; but a garden is a work of art, and art implies selection. It is true that there are plants, such as many kinds of roses, which seem to adapt themselves to almost any kind of garden. There are also certain simple plants that can sometimes be used with tremendous effect in a highly sophisticated design. I will never forget the charm of some potted pink geraniums in the garden of the Museum of Modern Art in New York some years ago. The garden was the setting for large pieces of modern sculpture; the ground was paved with crushed marble; there was a glooming mass of cryptomeria. Altogether the picture was as far removed from a cottage garden as it is possible to imagine, and yet there were the pots of pink geraniums, and I cannot think of anything else that would have been so utterly right. Perhaps it was their simplicity that was needed, but it took consummate skill to use them; it would have been easy merely to cheapen the garden.

It is impossible to make hard and fast rules for the selection of plants; one can only make general suggestions.

### Foliage Texture

The foliage texture is important, as is the grouping of different intensities of green. Sometimes a coarse-textured plant is appropriate, so that when one reads in a book or catalog that the leaves of a certain plant are coarse, this is not necessarily a strike against it. If the house is of rough fieldstone, a strong, shaggy shrub or tree may be just what is needed, instead of glossy, manicured material.

It is often a mistake in a small garden, where there is not enough distance to give perspective, to mass large plants; the result tends to be monotony and the loss of character in individual shrubs. Azaleas are often massed in places where they would be much more effective singly, or in very small groups. Shrubs with an interesting structure, such as black haw and dogwood, should not be jumbled in with other material so that their picturesque quality is lost.

Plants that retain their untamed woodland quality, such as mountain laurel, should not be placed beside formal looking plants such as certain varieties of juniper and yew.

Often the effect of contrasting types of foliage can be studied better in a small specialty garden, such as a herb garden, than in a collection of large plants. In a well-stocked herb garden there is an amazing range of texture and shades of green; the eye can take it in in a small area and go from there to an evaluation of plant textures on a larger scale.

## Many Criteria

Many things influence one's judgment of a plant. There is the professional reaction of the botanist, the horticulturist, the florist, and the landscape architect; and there is the reaction of the layman whose likes and dislikes have not been conditioned by a professional point of view. There is also the little bit of nostalgia, or sentiment, that resides in nearly everyone and surrounds a particular plant with a special aura.

I know, for instance, that I am quite incapable of looking at a rhododendron with complete objectivity. I grew up in a part of the world that was too hot for rhododendrons, and I saw them for the first time near the summit of Ceylon's highest mountain at dawn. We had left the hotel an hour or two after midnight, and as we neared the end of our climb, the lush tropical growth and the still, humid air of the lower slopes disappeared. A chilly wind was blowing. It was not quite light, and the twisted black shapes of tree rhododendrons began to emerge. Dawn broke, and great clusters of magenta blooms burst from the scarred old wood. No matter what rhododendron specimen confronts me, I cannot quite separate it from that first sharp impact on a cold, bare, windy mountain top.

A novice should not be ashamed of his judgment, or made to feel inferior by criticism. A painter does not learn to paint overnight, and no one can expect to become skilled with plants until he works with them. To do so is quite different from merely looking at pictures of them, or observing them in flower shows. In time, the kind of feeling is developed that comes only with experience. And of course one can become over-precious about selecting plants; this can give just as unfortunate results as planting them helter-skelter.

## A Weed Is a Plant Out of Place

It is also important to remember that a weed is a plant out of place. Many esteemed garden plants are nuisance plants in some parts of the world; the calla lily and lantana are two examples. The right plant for the right place is not necessarily a horticultural aristocrat. The object of making a garden is to achieve an over-all aesthetic effect in a given situation, and in doing so a tough old friend, or even a handsome one-time enemy, is much better than a sickly specimen, no matter how well-advertised or how rare. This advice is particularly pertinent in those city gardens where poor air circulation and noxious fumes are serious problems and the gardener cannot grow many of the plants he admires.

It is unfortunate that many useful plants that will grow easily under a wide range of conditions have been labeled weeds, or classified as inferior. It is still more unfortunate that many persons who are forced to live with them feel a little ashamed. Rather they should bend their energy to using them creatively. The tree-of-Heaven (*Ailanthus*) is a case in point. From coast to coast it is known contemptuously as a weed, though many thousands of acres would be destitute of green without it and millions of persons would never hear a bird sing in a tree. Its great drooping frond-like leaves impart a feeling of tropical luxuriance to grimy city lots. Instead of fighting the ailanthus, and struggling to make a garden with material such as arborvitae that is woefully unhappy in sooty air, how much more sensible to create a garden style in key with the tree that will grow there.

To take an extreme example of the usefulness of a weed plant, I have seen purslane doing a noble job in a planter on a sidewalk in a part of a big city where a heavy population of children and domestic animals would be death to most growing things. In this inhospitable environment, on a hot summer day, the fat fleshy leaves of this homely but exuberantly healthy plant were a lush oasis.

In New York City, the most truly genre gardens are usually owned by Italians. In walled-in courts more Mediterranean in flavor than gardens of the north Atlantic seaboard, they wisely and naturally grow figs and peaches and grape vines and sweet basil. The garden may belong to a tenement on the edge of the Bowery, but it is always refreshingly honest and sincere.

The gardener restricted by his environment, or his purse, should learn to look at plants with a fresh eye, and evaluate them for their intrinsic worth to him, regardless of whether their zest for survival has made them unfashionable or even despised. With this approach, he will find that making a garden under any conditions can become an exciting quest and a creative endeavor.

Nor will he find himself in undistinguished company. Gertrude Jekyll, who, around the turn of the century, profoundly influenced garden art in England, is said to have had her interest in garden design aroused when a factory worker in a northern manufacturing town advertised for help in making a window box. The box was to be about three feet by ten inches and it was to contain a rock garden, as full of interest as possible. Miss Jekyll replied and a correspondence followed, with, it is recorded, as much enthusiasm on Miss Jekyll's part as she later gave to the large and famous gardens in which she collaborated with Edwin Lutyens, a leading architect of the period. I do not know what Miss Jekyll put in the factory town window box, but I am quite sure that the last thing to concern her would be a plant's horticultural status. Indeed, she was known for her liking of simple flowers.

## Plant Lists

Plants lists are undeniably valuable as a reference, but I sometimes think that the gardener who sets too much store by lists is somewhat in the position of a traveler who pays more attention to his guidebook than to the objects he sees on his travels. Another approach, and not at all a bad one, is to observe plants and then to find out all you can about ones that attract you. Your interest at first may be restricted to a very few, but that doesn't matter; in fact, from both the aesthetic and the practical point of view, it may even be an advantage. Underplanting usually looks better than overplanting and is considerably easier to correct; also, you will have fewer failures to discourage you.

In using lists, it should be remembered that plant authorities often disagree. This is partly because of the different conditions under which specimens have been observed, and partly a simple difference of opinion. A plantsman is learning till the end of his life, and as you, the reader, become more knowledgeable, you will develop theories based on *your* experience.

## Chapter II

# TREES

The owner of a small garden lives intimately with his trees. A big tree can be as prominent as the house itself; indeed, if the house is small, and the tree is in front or to one side, the tree can overshadow the house and be the first thing a newcomer notices, the feature that leaps to mind when he describes the property.

The young trees that a new owner plants may some day, well within the years when he will be enjoying his garden, develop into specimens that dominate the rest of the planting and compel attention. Just one beautiful tree can be the keynote for a whole garden. The house will need refurbishing from time to time, but a good tree will simply gather distinction with the years. It is strange, then, how often a tree is bought almost casually, while at the same time a great deal of thought goes into the choice of a minor shrub.

## Size of Tree

It may be questioned whether some of the trees included in the lists at the end of this section will not eventually become too big for the sized gardens we are discussing. A great deal depends on the height of the house and the type of garden that is planned, but, generally speaking, it is amazing what a big tree a small property will stand. The important thing is to know what you are doing, and not plant several outsize trees, or plant them too close together.

## Rate of Growth

Trees vary a great deal in their rate of growth. Some kinds grow rapidly at first, and slowly after they have reached a certain size. Others grow slowly throughout their life. The same kind of tree will vary in rate of growth and ultimate size under

148

different conditions. The maximum size given for the same tree in lists compiled by several knowledgeable authorities often varies enormously. The best thing to do when faced with conflicting statements of this kind is to average the difference or consult local experience.

## Cost

The importance of cost is self-evident for most people. Prices of trees rise sharply above a certain size, and anyone new to plant shopping may feel them to be prohibitive; he forgets how much he is planning to spend for a household item that will wear out in a few years. The price of even an expensive tree can be dissipated very rapidly on a few medium-sized shrubs, and in the long run the money is usually better spent on a well grown tree. Most shrubs reach their maximum size much faster than trees, and planted as small specimens will not take long to fill out.

Another solution, if you have over-extended yourself on a tree, is to use inexpensive shrubs at first, or even large shrubby perennials or annuals, and replace them gradually by better material. The local market is the best guide to low-priced temporary material. In the North, the tender lantana and certain mallows (both perennial in warm climates), make rapid, shrub-like growth in a season and serve this purpose very well, since there are fewer heartaches when frost fells them than if they have to be uprooted in full vigor to make place for a more costly replacement. The castor bean, growing from a seed planted outdoors in spring, will be six feet high at the end of summer.

The point that cannot be made too emphatically is that nothing does more to make a garden look as though it is really on its way than completed construction work and one or two good-sized trees. This establishes the framework of the garden and provides an impetus to complete the picture.

## A Young Tree Can Be Deceptive

The trees in the nursery are the local selections of a huge slice of plant life, some of it native to America, some of it gathered from the far corners of the earth, some of it the fruit of years of patient work by plant breeders. And each kind of tree possesses distinctive qualities that determine its propriety for a particular place. The true character of a tree, however, the thing that makes it right for a special purpose, is often only feebly apparent in the nursery, where immature specimens stand balled and burlapped ready for sale, or are still in a row in the nursery field.

Confronted with a bewildering array of trees, you may often find it very difficult to avoid making a hit-and-miss choice. The tree that is in every way best for you may not be the most eye-catching one at the time of purchase, and it is easy to lose your heart to a pretty thing that has everything against it for your garden except immediate appeal.

### Remember the Plan

This is the time to think firmly of your plan. In fact, it is a good thing to have it with you, to strengthen your resolve if temptation threatens. For, if you have read the first part of this book, you will not be sallying forth to a nursery *until* you have made your plan. And if you have made your plan, you will be quite clear about certain attributes of your tree.

### Large, Medium, Small?

Is it, for instance, to be large, medium or small? Do you want it primarily for shade, for fruit, to act as a screen, or purely for something to look at? Do you passionately want it to be ever-green?

If you are clear on these matters, you will know whether your choice automatically eliminates what are known as needle-leaf trees. In the South, many trees are evergreen; but in the North the only evergreen trees belong to the great class known as conifers, all of which have narrow, needle-like leaves and are known as needle-leaf as distinct from broad-leaf trees.

### Shade Trees

If you want fruit, you obviously will not want a conifer. And though a big conifer may cast a long shadow, it is not, in the usual sense of the word, a shade tree. "Shade tree" is really a rather vague term, but the most general meaning is a tree with a high spreading canopy of branches under which one can sit. The pagoda tree or Chinese scholar tree *(Sophora japonica)* no doubt gets its common name from the uses with which this tree is associated. Characters in old-fashioned folksy literature are always foregathering under elms and oaks and maples and chestnuts and lindens; therefore anyone who has read at all has a list of shade trees at his fingertips.

Obviously, a tree densely clothed with large leaves, such as the Norway maple, gives heavier shade than a tree with narrow leaves or light feathery foliage, such as the honey locust, the albizzia or the jacaranda. When the tree has heavy horizontal branches some feet from the ground, a characteristic of the aforementioned pagoda tree and many of the oaks, a veritable roof is created. Other trees again, such as the shagbark hickory, give a high dappled shade, ideal for rhododendrons and azaleas. The great shade trees of the northern hemisphere hold their leaves horizontally, or parallel to the ground, whereas in Australia the eucalyptus trees provide very poor shade because not only are the leaves commonly long and narrow but are held with the blade at right angles to the ground to conserve moisture in a hot climate.

A needle-leaf tree will therefore be your choice only if you have one or all of the following objectives: 1—to have a green tree in winter; 2—to provide a dense, year-round screen or windbreak; 3—pure ornament.

## Practical Points

And now, having considered your tree from a design and functional angle, you will want to be clear on a number of practical points. You may know exactly what you would like to have, but a tree, no matter how desirable, that will not grow in your garden is a pretty useless thing for you. It is a good idea to check the following list of questions:

1. Is the tree to be planted in sun or shade?
2. Is the soil in my garden wet, dry, acid, alkaline?
3. Is my garden subject to strong winds, making it unwise to plant a tree with brittle wood?
4. Are there drains that might be clogged by the vigorous,

water-seeking roots of certain trees, such as willows, poplars, and the silver maple?

5. Is the tree to be planted close to the house, where low branches will be a nuisance? Should I choose a tree such as the tulip tree, with a straight clean trunk and a high canopy to shade the roof? Or do I want a screen tree, when a low branching habit will be valuable?

6. Do I have the labor to keep the garden tidy if I plant a tree that constantly sheds leaves, such as the willow or black walnut?

7. Is the tree I want subject to any serious pest or disease in my location?

8. Do I need a quick-growing tree?

9. Is the tree to be grown in or near a lawn? Grass will not grow in heavy shade. A lawn tree should have open foliage and should not be predominantly surface rooting.

Other questions you might ask yourself are:

1. Do I value a tree more for its color in fall than for its appearance the rest of the year?

2. Is the pattern of the branches in winter important to me, or do I pack up and go south in the cold weather?

3. Is the shadow of the tree to fall on foliage, where it will be largely lost, or on a paved, graveled, or grassed surface?

4. If the tree is a flowering tree, will early, mid-season, or late flowers be best in the scheme of my garden?

## Needle-leaf Trees

Though the kinds of needle-leaf, cone-bearing trees used in landscape work, especially in a small garden, are much fewer than those of deciduous trees, there are sharp distinctions between them and many gruesome mistakes are made because the characteristics of the different varieties are not known. A coniferous evergreen tree is as permanent as anything you will plant in your garden, so it is worth taking a little time to consider which one you want.

The four big groups of trees in this class are fir *(Abies),* spruce *(Picea),* pine *(Pinus),* and hemlock *(Tsuga).* White cedar *(Chamaecyparis),* juniper *(Juniperus),* arborvitae *(Thuja),* and yew *(Taxus)*, though they attain the size of trees, are more often represented in gardens by shrub forms, which may be any size from dwarf to very large.

In addition to the above big groups, in all of which there are many species and varieties, there are a few highly individual cone-bearing trees that are either alone of their kind, or represented by very few species or varieties. These include cryptomeria, umbrella pine, Douglas fir, larch, and swamp cypress.

Of the names mentioned above, the ones that nearly everyone knows are fir, spruce and pine. Fir and spruce are often confused, and I have been in parts of the Rockies where local residents spoke of all three simply as pines.

The purpose of these notes is not to discuss botanical differences, but to try to clarify the place of the major conifers in a small home garden. Let us take them in turn.

FIR *(Abies)*. The needles of the fir are less prickly than those of the spruce. They are also attached more firmly to the stem, and because of this quality firs make superior Christmas trees.

The firs are big trees, conical, broadly conical, or narrowly conical. The color of the foliage varies in depth and in some forms is blue or blue-green. The native white fir *(Abies concolor)*, a beautiful tree with a bluish cast, is one of the biggest, and, since it grows rapidly, is not a good choice for a small garden. The Korean fir *(Abies koreana)* grows slowly, and is also smaller at maturity than most firs. It is stiff and formal. The cork fir *(Abies arizonica)* is a native of Arizona and a relatively small tree. The Nikko fir *(Abies homolepis)* is a valuable Japanese species. The balsam fir *(Abies balsamea)*, the best of the Christmas trees, is unsatisfactory under cultivation.

The firs available differ locally. Decide whether you want one with bright green needles, or one with a bluish cast; this is important. Also check the rate of growth; some kinds grow so slowly that ultimate height is not of much significance.

SPRUCE *(Picea)*. One of the most popular trees in the small home garden has long been the blue spruce. Not only is it grown as a large specimen, but infant trees turn up frequently in foundation plantings.

It is a stiff tree, and in a small area its nature is to remain aloof from its companions in a sort of grim isolation. It should be used with great discrimination. When it has gotten out of hand, or become ragged in a foundation planting, it can sometimes be shaped into a sort of giant bonsai. Plate 19 shows a blue spruce that was changed from a monstrosity beside a porch into a picturesque plant.

Not all spruces are stiff, however. All are conical in shape, though some are narrower than others. Most grow to be very big trees; many deteriorate with age. One of the best for small gardens is the Serbian spruce *(Picea omorika)*, narrowly conical, with rich foliage and drooping branches. The Oriental spruce *(Picea orientalis)* is another fine species.

Both fir and spruce are hard to use, from a landscape point of view, on flat territory; they look much better in a hollow in undulating land. It is understandable that persons who have grown up in mountain country, or have the forests of Europe in their background, should feel a nostalgic longing for one of these trees; but it is unfair to a tree to put it where its natural beauty is caricatured.

PINE *(Pinus)*. The pines, with their greater variety of form, are much more adaptable in small gardens than either the spruce or the fir. They also have a much wider geographical range. Many pines are identified with certain parts of the country, and gardeners in these areas should consider good native varieties.

All pines require sun. Many cannot endure exposure, but the Austrian pine *(Pinus nigra)*, the Japanese black pine *(Pinus thunbergi)*, and the Scotch pine *(Pinus sylvestris)* are notable exceptions.

The Austrian pine is a stiff tree, less beautiful than many other pines, but it makes an excellent windbreak.

The Japanese black pine is outstanding for shore gardens, since it is not harmed by salt-laden winds. Both are rather coarse trees.

The Scotch pine is one of the most picturesque of the pines. The bark is almost orange. As the tree grows, the lower branches tend to die and must be removed; this makes the beautiful trunk a much more conspicuous feature of the tree than it is in many pines. The foliage is blue-green, and especially intense in winter. If a single pine is to be grown, the Scotch pine is hard to beat.

White pine *(Pinus strobus)* is the most popular native pine. It grows rapidly and, unrestrained, eventually becomes a huge tree. It can, however, be kept within bounds by correct pruning. Cutting should never be done on the bare part of a twig between needles, but in the middle of a needled twig. The needles of the white pine are fine in texture, and a stand of white pine at dusk gives the illusion of velvet.

The Japanese red pine *(Pinus densiflora)*. Among pines that have been introduced from the Orient, several of them are outstanding and merit attention. The Japanese red pine is many trunked from the base, with a flattish top. The bark is orange-red and most striking. It is hardy to New England and southern Ontario.

The Lace-bark pine *(Pinus bungeana)* from China, has a most unusual bark, which gives the impression of a patchwork in soft pastel colors. Though it eventually becomes a big tree, it is slow growing. It is hardy into western New York and Massachusetts, and anyone enterprising enough to get it will have a feature tree that will give quality to his garden.

The Chinese white pine *(Pinus armandi)* is notable for its pale gray, almost white bark. It is said to be hardy in Massachusetts, but it does not appear to be well known and may be hard to get. I would like very much to know whether this is the arresting white-trunked pine which grew on the Coal Hill near the Summer Palace in Peking some twenty years ago. I am mentioning this out-of-the-way pine because the only way to get new and lovely trees into gardens is for people to ask for them and so encourage their growth in nurseries.

The Mugo pine *(Pinus mugo)*. This little Swiss mountain pine is usually dwarf or bushy in cultivation. It is valuable in landscape work, and especially useful near the shore, where it is resistant to the effect of harsh ocean winds.

HEMLOCK *(Tsuga)*. The hemlock, though a great tree, is an adaptable one for a small garden. At any size, and under almost any conditions, its feathery foliage is graceful; even a little stunted specimen misplanted in a city yard, while refusing to grow and thicken, will retain a delicate fern-like appearance. On properties of any size, it makes an excellent shorn hedge. A single specimen does not look as lonely as a solitary spruce or fir. It branches to the ground and makes a fine screen tree.

The kind most commonly grown is the Canadian hemlock (*Tsuga canadensis*). The Carolina hemlock (*Tsuga caroliniana*) is smaller and stiffer. There is also a western hemlock (*Tsuga heterophylla*).

DOUGLAS FIR (*Pseudotsuga douglasi*). This immense lumber tree of the north Pacific Coast and eastward to the mountains of Colorado is represented by several forms, some of which are useful in even small gardens. Dr. Donald Wyman, of the Arnold Arboretum, recommends pruning and shearing it for hedges.

CRYPTOMERIA. *Crytomeria japonica* is the only species of the genus. It is better known on the Pacific Coast than in the East, where it is doubtfully hardy north of New York. It is a narrow tree, with short branches, and the cinnamon-brown trunk from which the bark peels in long strips is conspicuous. It comes from Japan, where it makes a world-famous contribution to the temple planting at Nikko. Though it is an authentic tree for a Japanese-style garden, it is highly individual and should be used with discrimination.

CEDAR (*Cedrus*). The name cedar is applied locally to a number of trees. No attempt is made here to list them. The only true cedars are *Cedrus*. None is native, and, unless propagated from selected specimens, none is reliably hardy in the northeastern states as far north as New England. The cedars are extremely valuable on the Pacific Coast and in parts of the South. They grow to be immense trees, with a huge spread at the base, and are included here because of their literary and historic significance, their popular appeal, and the fact that even a very small garden in, for instance, California, is not infrequently dominated by a cedar.

The two famous cedars are the cedar of Lebanon (*Cedrus libanotica*) and the drooping Deodar cedar (*Cedrus deodora*). Anyone acquiring a small property on which one of these great trees was anywhere near maturity would not want to plant much else. Apart from their size, the cedars have a lordly character that defies competition. They are native to the Near and Far East, and one associates them with the fragrance of such plants as jasmine and musk roses. It would be inappropriate to surround them with stiff little shrubs.

LARCH *(Larix).* The larch is a graceful tree, and there are not many species or varieties. It is unusual among conifers in that it is deciduous. The most ornamental is the Japanese larch *(Larix kaempferi).* In some sections the needles turn such a brilliant yellow in fall that the tree looks literally like a "burning bush." The young growth in spring suggests a delicately threaded necklace.

BALD CYPRESS *(Taxodium).* The deciduous bald cypress *(Taxodium distichum)* is known in different parts of the country as black cypress, buck cypress, cow cypress, red cypress, southern cypress, swamp cypress, white cypress and yellow cypress. This gives some indication of the variation in bark color under different conditions.

In the swamplands of the south it forms projections or "knees" from the roots, through which air is presumably admitted. In well-drained upland soil the knees are absent. In spite of this remarkable example of adaptation, the bald cypress proudly retains its distinctive character under a variety of growing conditions. The foliage is light and feathery, and the small round cones when young may be beautiful with delicate pastel tints.

The bald cypress would not be easy to fit into a general planting on a small property, but it would be valuable as the dominant tree in a certain type of garden. It is not a Japanese tree, but it fits in very well in a Japanese garden. It should be planted without competition from deciduous shrubs of the mock orange—kerria—spirea type. In an artificial setting, it belongs more with manicured lawns and quality ericaceous shrubs, such as azaleas, pieris and enkianthus. It becomes a big tree eventually.

*Taxodium distichum,* though native to the South, has a wide climatic range, being cultivated as far north as Boston, through most of the mid-Atlantic states north to Indiana and Illinois, and on the Pacific Coast.

UMBRELLA PINE *(Sciadopitys verticillata).* The umbrella pine is another distinctive conifer, a native of Japan, and alone in its genus. It is hardy into Massachusetts and western New York. Though a big tree in its native habitat, it is slow-growing in this country and may be planted safely in small gardens. It is a wonderfully handsome tree, the whorls of coarse leaves being reminiscent of the turbulent pines in a Van Gogh painting. It is another tree that should not be used indiscriminately in a mixed planting.

## Broad-leaf Trees

These are the deciduous trees of the cold North and similar type trees that hold their leaves throughout the year in the warmer temperatures of the South. They are much more numerous than the conifers, and suited to many more garden purposes. In fact, the group is so huge and varied that any discussion of it poses a problem in a small book, especially since the existence of micro-climates limits the usefulness of certain trees even when they are well within the broad climatic zone for which they are suited.

## Tree Lists

Tree lists are perhaps more useful than most plant lists because trees are too permanent and important to be changed every few years. Lists therefore supply a broad base from which to work and help you to avoid a faulty choice. In the two following lists, "A" gives well known shade or ornamental trees represented by several or many varieties and with a wide geographical range. "B" is confined to trees which, though well known and important in certain areas, are represented by only one or two varieties of any significance. A number of trees in list "B" are not widely distributed. Many beautiful trees have, of necessity, been omitted from both lists.

Symbols are used to designate trees that are drought-resistant, tolerant of or partial to wet ground, and good subjects for the seashore.

A.   TREES WITH WIDE DISTRIBUTION

* Drought Resistant.        ** Wet Ground.        † Shore.

### ACER, MAPLE

The maples are a large and useful group of native and foreign trees, with a wide geographical range and soil tolerance. Following is a selection of kinds that might very well come with an established property, or are especially suitable for small gardens, or fit a specific situation, or have drawbacks of which the gardener should be aware:

## 1. MEDIUM TO LARGE

The silver maple *(Acer saccharinum)*,** so called because the undersides of the leaves are silvery. A pretty tree, more airy looking than many maples. Grows rapidly in sun or partial shade, but the wood is brittle and the roots may clog drains.

The Norway maple *(Acer platanoides),*† widely planted and a dense shade tree. Difficult to grow anything under it and the shallow feeding roots often interfere with the growth of plants near it. Many horticultural forms, of which Schwedler's maple, with purple-red leaves, is one of the most popular. The Norway maple stands city conditions better than most maples, and is useful in gardens near the coast. Is also said to like lime, though it certainly flourishes in soil that is not alkaline. Grows rapidly.

The red maple *(Acer rubrum)*,** native to low and swampy areas, but quite tolerant of drier conditions. Grows rapidly. The brilliant red color comes early in fall. A valuable shade tree.

The sycamore maple *(Acer pseudoplatanus),*† a splendid shade tree for exposed situations, including salt-laden gales. Good soil tolerance, but should not be planted in shallow soil. Does not color in fall.

The sugar maple *(Acer saccharum)*, a magnificent native shade tree, with brilliant fall color. Likes sun and open, clear air; not suitable for city or shore. Growth rate moderate to slow. Widely grown throughout the eastern part of the country, has a flavor of New England, and fits well into a colonial type garden.

The bigleaf maple *(Acer macrophyllum)*, an excellent shade tree on the Pacific Coast, does not do well in the East. Fall color is bright yellow. Has the largest leaves of any maple, and this may be a strike against it in a very small garden.

The box-elder *(Acer negundo)*,* many undesirable qualities, including a tendency to clog drains. Its merits are that it grow rapidly, will stand dry soil and severe cold; sometimes useful for a quick screen, or as a temporary tree while a slower-growing kind is becoming established.

2. SMALL TO MEDIUM

The hedge or field maple *(Acer campestre)*,* excellent for a screen or hedge. Has a dense growth and stands severe pruning. Grows slowly, likes sun or partial shade, prefers dry soil, does well in poor soil or sand. Does not color as vividly as some maples.

The vine maple *(Acer circinatum)*, a native of the Pacific Coast, with a picturesque twisting growth habit. Will grow in light shade. Foliage dense and autumn color good.

The Amur maple *(Acer ginnala)*, a valuable large shrub or small tree, with dense foliage, bright red fruits in the summer, and brilliant autumn color. Extremely hardy.

### BETULA, BIRCH

The birches, with their distinctive bark and lacy foliage, are delightful in small gardens. Some kinds are short-lived, but a short-lived, quick-growing form can be very useful in a new garden, while slower-growing permanent material is becoming established. This is particularly true of some of the housing developments, where the ground has been stripped bare for building and there are no big trees in the surrounding area. In situations like this quick-growing trees of almost any kind are desperately needed.

The cherry birch, or sweet birch *(Betula lenta)*, dark, smooth bark like the bark of a cherry tree. Grows to be a big tree, has good fall color, is hardy into Maine. Likes moist, well-drained soil in sun or partial shade. Is one of the longer-lived birches.

The river birch or red birch *(Betula nigra)*,** not long-lived in the North, but valuable for its ability to grow in wet places. Can become a big tree.

The canoe, white, or paper birch *(Betula papyrifera)*, the famous and beautiful white-trunked birch of northern woods. Will not grow as far south as Pennsylvania, and does not like an exposed site. Often confused with the European white birch *(Betula pendula)*.

The gray birch *(Betula populifolia)*,** a many-trunked, white-barked tree with triangular black markings. Short-lived, but highly recommended as a temporary tree. Grows rapidly, is extremely graceful, thrives on dry poor soil as well as wet soil.

*Photograph by Bee Pancoast Weber*

Plate 19.   A blue spruce that was crowded, ragged and unsightly before it was shaped by Landscape Architect Dina Bauman into this ornamental specimen. (Page 154.)

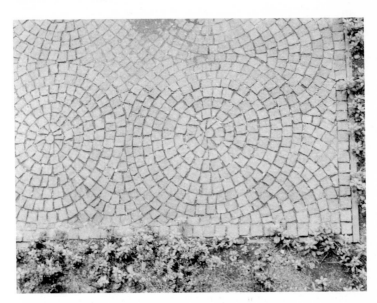

*Photograph by Bee Pancoast Weber*

Plate 20.   Texture speaks for itself. Fish-scale paving with small granite blocks combines pleasingly with a border of pachysandra.

*Don Walp, Landscape Architect; photograph by Gottscho-Schleisner, Inc.*

Plate 21. Planting within the area of the terrace brings the garden close to the large window of the living room. Note the intricate brickwork in the curving, eight-inch-wide wall.

*Photograph by Gottscho-Schleisner, Inc.*

Plate 22, opposite: The simple white picket fence separating this garden from the adjoining property illustrates the use of structural material that is in harmony with neighboring buildings. In this way, not only is the appearance of the street improved, but the enclosed property is made to seem larger. By setting the fence back a little, space is provided for a low planting to soften the hard line of the concrete curb. A small-leafed variety of wintercreeper *(Euonymus)* would be excellent here for year-round effect.

*By courtesy of The New York Botanical Garden; photograph by Gottscho-Schleisner, Inc.*

Plate 23. This traditional herb garden, designed for The New York Botanical Garden by The Herb Society of America, measures approximately 44′ x 58′ but could be carried out at a much smaller scale.

The centerpiece is a knot garden (Figure 51).

The herbs massed in the wide beds that form the outer rim of the garden include angelica, betony (lamb's-ears), black snakeroot, chives, germander, hyssop, lavender, marjoram, nepeta, sage, savory, senna, southernwood, sweet basil, tansy, thyme, wild bergamot, and wild ginger. Also in the garden, though not visible in the picture, is a black mulberry (*Morus nigra*).

## CORNUS, DOGWOOD

The flowering dogwood (*Cornus florida*), too well known to require description. It acquires remarkable beauty with age; ancient specimens are spectacular for their silhouette. Intolerant of soot and not a good choice for cities, where it tends to peter out after a few years, though it continues to be planted hopefully by many gardeners. Can become a big tree, but more often of medium size. There are pink and white-flowered forms.

The Japanese dogwood (*Cornus kousa*), almost in the large shrub class, but may be considered a tree in small gardens. Blooms later than *Cornus florida*, and the flowers are usually white. Somewhat less hardy than *C. florida*.

The Cornelian Cherry (*Cornus mas*), hardy into Massachusetts, a perfect specimen for a small garden. The yellow flowers are like small tassels, totally unlike the showy bracts of *Cornus florida*. They appear before the leaves at about the same time as forsythia blooms. This sturdy, disease-resistant little tree has great character and a great look of permanence. It is borderline shrub-tree in size. Though it retains its identity among a mass of plants, it does not deserve crowding.

The Pacific Dogwood (*Cornus nuttalli*), does not adapt well to the East but is spectacular throughout the Pacific Coast to southern California. Flowers normally white. May become a large tree.

## CRATAEGUS, HAWTHORN

The hawthorn is the "May tree" of England, and a familiar plant in literature. It is a large group of big shrubs and small trees, with thorns that are sometimes long and sharp. The thorns make it an excellent barrier plant, but species with dangerous thorns should be used with discrimination where there are children. The pink or white flowers are lovely in spring, and the clusters of bright red fruits, like miniature apples, attractive in winter. The growth is often extremely picturesque. Some kinds are badly troubled by insect pests, and gardeners should check this weakness in the variety they are proposing to buy. Some have good fall color. In addition to the species, there are many horticultural forms. Only a very few kinds, with especially distinctive qualities, are mentioned here; there are many other excellent hawthorns.

The Kansas hawthorn (*Crataegus coccinioides*), natural habitat from Indiana to Kansas. White flowers, exceptionally large fruit, good fall color.

The cockspur thorn (*Crataegus crus-galli*), native to northeastern America and outstanding for its shiny, leathery leaves and decorative winter silhouette. Top is usually flat and spreading, with a great deal of twiggy growth. Clusters of small white flowers look rather like coral. Fruits a good size, may hang on all winter. Thorns long and angry. The cockspur thorn makes a splendid hedge and a good city tree. A row of cockspur thorns in winter can give the effect of a frieze against the sky or a masonry wall.

The English hawthorn (*Crataegus oxyacantha*), most popular in pink- and red-flowered varieties, of which Paul's Scarlet is one of the best known. A lovely thing in spring, but too often late summer finds the foliage unsightly through the attack of insect enemies. Grown from coast to coast and is reasonably hardy.

The Washington hawthorn (*Crataegus phaenopyrum*), an excellent small ornamental for city and suburb. The bright red fruits are distasteful to birds, so remain conspicuous all winter, in big cities they are sometimes the only colorful winter fruits. The foliage may not color in the city, but normally it is good.

### FAGUS, BEECH

Both the American beech (*Fagus grandifolia*) and the English beech (*Fagus sylvatica*) grow to be very big trees, with a huge spread at the base, and this should be remembered in considering their location on a small property. A large tree near a boundary line may be a source of pleasure (or, one must admit, occasional annoyance) to two or three owners. They are extraordinarily handsome trees. The American beech is a little hardier than the English beech, with lighter bark. There are many forms of the English beech, narrow and columnar or weeping in growth habit, some purple-leafed and some with finely cut leaves. There are few things more beautiful in winter than the bark of a beech. The fact that the roots are close to the surface, making planting under it difficult, does not seem a pertinent objection, for who would want to grow anything under a beech?

### FRAXINUS, ASH

The ash is a widely distributed group of trees, with several adaptable, easily grown species. This kind of tree is always useful to have on one's list, but it is not recommended for small gardens in the East when better trees are available. On the Pacific Coast, however, the Oregon ash (*Fraxinus oregona*) is an important shade tree. The velvet ash or Arizona ash *(Fraxinus velutina)* is grown in California and the Southwest. It is very useful for dry saline and alkaline soil.

## ILEX, HOLLY

The holly is known to everyone, and by proper selection it may be widely grown. The varieties run into hundreds and any one variety may have quite a limited range. It is therefore impossible to make brief, general recommendations as to the kind of holly to grow. It *is* possible, however, to recommend a red-fruiting evergreen holly as one of the most distinguished looking of plants. Hollies are long-lived, and an ancient, well-grown specimen is beautiful beyond compare. On the Pacific Coast, the lustrous-leafed English hollies do much better than they do in the East. The plant is dioecious, therefore a male and a female specimen must be grown to produce berries.

## MAGNOLIA, MAGNOLIA

It is always something of a shock that a tree with the exotic qualities of the magnolia should bestow its largesse over such a wide range of territory; it eschews only the driest and coldest sections of the country. It is mostly valued for its white, pink, or pinkish-purple flowers, which in some kinds are of spectacular size, but in the southern magnolia *(Magnolia grandiflora)* the great dark glossy leaves with furry-brown undersides would alone make it a valuable specimen tree. The "cones" of scarlet seeds, briefly present after the fruits split, are dramatic in some varieties.

The southern magnolia *(Magnolia grandiflora)*, is grown widely in the South and in California. In the East it becomes hazardous from Philadelphia northward. The huge white flowers in late spring and early summer are fragrant. May become a very big tree.

The saucer magnolia *(Magnolia soulangeana)*, thoroughly hardy in the vicinity of New York City, where it flowers profusely under adverse conditions of soil and light. Leaves light green and do not have the gloss of the southern magnolia. There are many varieties, and the cup-shaped flowers range from white through shades of pinkish purple. Bark often very light, almost white, making the several trunks an attractive feature throughout the year. In the New York area, the flowers smother the tree in April, before the leaves appear. A small tree, with picturesque growth, and invaluable for the city gardener.

The star magnolia *(Magnolia stellata)*, shrub-like in growth even if it attains the size of a small tree. The petals of the white or pink fragrant flowers are straplike and reflexed. It also grows in the vicinity of New York City, but with less exuberance than the saucer magnolia.

The sweet bay *(Magnolia virginiana),* * * grows into New England, where it is smaller than in the South. Flowers later than the southern and saucer magnolias. The medium-sized white flowers are fragrant. Is very useful for wet ground.

### MALUS, CRABAPPLE

Crabapples are a variety of apple with a small, acid fruit. The group is very big, with tremendous variation in the texture and shape of the leaves and the size and color of the fruit. Even the bark varies somewhat, and many contain shades of pink and purple; typically, though, it is the mottled "apple tree" bark which is so beautiful in a garden. The leaves may be firm, quite large, and glossy, with a fairly smooth edge; or they may be incised, as in cut-leaf forms; or they may be rather thin, without much substance or character; or they may be a handsome reddish green or reddish bronze. The fruit varies from about a quarter of an inch in diameter to about two inches, and may be orange, yellow, or red, translucent or opaque. The flowers may be single, double, or semi-double, and usually appear in May. Often they are fragrant. Sometimes the buds of white flowers are pink, or white tipped with red.

Most crabapples are small trees, but at least one, the Sargent crab, is a shrub. In shape, they may be spreading, upright, or pendulous. Some varieties are more adaptable to environment than others. The color of the flowers in some kinds fades rapidly. Not all kinds fruit every year.

This general description indicates the wide choice available and suggests features to look for when choosing a crab. Popular kinds include Hopa, with profuse rose flowers and large fruits; the vase-shaped tea crab *(Malus hupehensis)*; Katherine, with large double flowers and more open branches than many crabs; the upright Arnold crab, with deep red flower buds contrasting with lighter blossoms; and the Sargent crab, a spreading mound-like shrub with white fragrant blossoms.

### PLATANUS, PLANE

One thinks of the plane tree more as a street tree, and a tree for large areas, than for small gardens. However, the London plane

*(Platanus acerifolia)* which is a natural hybrid of the American and Oriental planes, is useful in cities because of its resistance to noxious air. It grows rapidly and provides vigorous foliage. The bark is an attractive mottled greenish-white. To many people its shedding bark and leaves in late summer are objectionable.

## POPULUS, POPLAR

The poplars include the famous columnar forms of Europe, the quaking aspens that are golden in the mountains of Utah (and other areas) in fall, and the tough cottonwoods of hot dry sections of the Midwest and Southwest. Poplars have vigorous, greedy, water-seeking roots, and should be avoided near foundations and drains. Certain kinds are useful in specific situations. For the small property, their greatest value is as a quick-growing screen, and as fillers and nurse plants while slower growing trees are becoming established.

The Lombardy poplar *(Populus nigra italica)*, columnar in shape, hardy, quick-growing, and resistant to smoke. The Simon poplar *(Populus simoni)*, another hardy, quick-growing, narrow poplar can be a substitute for the Lombardy unless smoke is a problem.

The quaking aspen *(Populus tremuloides)*, a dancing tree, with wonderful yellow color in fall. The trunks are almost white. A tree for grouping in a woodland garden. In the Rockies it is a nurse tree for conifers, and there is a familiar rhythm of a burned conifer forest, a spectacular stand of quaking aspens, and, completing the cycle, the crowding out of the aspens by the new conifers.

## PRUNUS, FLOWERING CHERRY

There are innumerable flowering cherries and they occupy a comparable place in garden design to crabapples. The Asiatic kinds flower early, before the leaves, and the native and European varieties a little later, with the leaves. They all need sun to flower well. Varieties of *Prunus serrulata* are the famous Oriental cherries, single or double flowered, fragrant or without fragrance. One of the most popular varieties is Kwanzan, but it is a clumsy tree beside the more delicate Higan cherry *(Prunus subhirtella)*, one of the earliest and most floriferous of the Oriental cherries. The weeping variety is particularly lovely.

Weeping flowering cherries are often grown as standards, on a straight stiff stem. These little artificial-looking trees are delightful in small, formal gardens, but wildly out of place if crowded in with other material.

A hybrid, Prunus "Hally Jolivette" is relatively new and especially lovely. The double flowers do not open all at once, but consecutively over a ten- to twenty-day period. It is a small tree with beautiful shape.

## QUERCUS, OAK

In the oaks we have another great group of foliage trees, enormously diversified in size, shape, habit of growth, and usefulness in the garden. Many of the oaks grown in American gardens are native, and many are identified with certain sections of the country. In the cold North, oaks are deciduous trees; in the South and in California the live oaks are one of the magnificent natural phenomena. In choosing an oak, gardeners are advised to consult local authorities. Only a very few kinds, noteworthy for special reasons, are mentioned here:

The swamp white oak *(Quercus bicolor),** native to the eastern and central parts of the country, valued for its toughness and adaptability to swampy soils. Picturesque.

The red oak *(Quercus borealis),* not hardy in the coldest sections of the country, very quick growing, transplants easily, tolerant of city air, has fine red autumn color.

The scarlet oak *(Quercus coccinea),* about the same climatic range as the red oak. An attractive lightness of growth and the fall color is magnificent. Difficult to transplant, and should be bought only from a reliable source where it has been correctly root-pruned. Admirers of the scarlet oak are willing to take a lot of trouble to establish it. A wide natural range.

The shingle oak *(Quercus imbricaria),*† grows slowly and a majestic shade tree, with orange-russet color in fall. Grows well near the shore. A little less hardy than the scarlet oak and the red oak. Recommended for shearing as a hedge.

The blackjack oak *(Quercus marilandica),** a small tree, valuable for its ability to grow in dry sand, barren clay, or poorly drained gravel. Too tender for the colder sections of the country.

The pin oak *(Quercus palustris),*** has a horizontal and, at the base, drooping habit of growth unusual in an oak. The leaves rather fine, and scarlet in fall. Transplants easily, grows well in cities, is at home in low and swampy land. Because of its unusual shape, a well-grown specimen should be studied before choosing it for the garden. Does not have a great open trunk like many oaks. Not hardy in the coldest sections of the country.

The willow oak *(Quercus phellos)*, has narrow, pointed leaves, smaller at maturity than the great oaks, easy to transplant. Fall color not outstanding, but is a nice tree for a garden. Not one of the hardiest oaks, but grows in southern New York and probably somewhat farther north on the coast.

The live oak *(Quercus virginiana)*, the famous dark-leafed evergreen oak of the South, where it is often draped with curtains of Spanish moss. For Southerners it needs no description, and Northerners cannot grow it. Deciduous near its northern limits.

### SALIX, WILLOW

There are many species and many varieties of willows. They are valuable for their tolerance of wet ground, for the ease and rapidity with which they can be grown, for the grace of weeping forms, and, in winter, for the color of yellow-stemmed varieties. They are dangerous near drains, and the dropping of leaves and small twigs makes them messy trees. There are situations, however, when no other tree is quite so right as a willow. In city gardens, the small pussy willow bush type *(Salix discolor)* is valuable.

The white willow *(Salix alba)*,** hardy in the coldest sections of the country. There is a yellow-twigged variety, and one with bright red twigs. The delicate etching of yellow twigs against a smoke-gray sky is one of winter's most beautiful sights. It is a shame to put such a willow where its silhouette is against a building and not against the open sky.

The Babylon weeping willow *(Salix babylonica)*,** not as hardy as a weeping variety of the white willow, *Salix alba tristis*, the golden weeping willow. There are other varieties of weeping willow, hardier than the Babylon and less hardy than the golden weeping willow.

The goat willow *(Salix caprea)*, a small tree and considered the best of the pussy willows. Hardy, but not in the coldest sections of the country.

The laurel willow *(Salix pentandra)*, a handsome tree, with larger, darker leaves than the typical willow.

### SORBUS, MOUNTAIN-ASH

There is no more brilliant sight on the coast of Maine than specimens of heavily-fruited mountain-ash in deep gardens sweeping down to the shore and perched on cliffs above the ocean. In August and September the trees stand out like beacons. On the Pacific Coast, in Portland and Oregon, the mountain-ash is also grown with great success. In many places, however, including the coast in the vicinity of Long Island, it is seriously subject to borers. Where it can be grown, the mountain-ash is a fine ornamental, branching high on a fairly straight clean stem.

The Korean mountain-ash *(Sorbus alnifolia)*,† considered to be one of the best varieties. Berries orange to scarlet. Larger than the American and European species and less hardy.

The European mountain-ash or rowan tree *(Sorbus aucuparia)*,† hardy in the coldest parts of the country and the most popular variety. Berries bright red, in large clusters.

The American mountain-ash *(Sorbus americana)*,† the smallest of the kinds mentioned. Fruits bright red, extremely hardy.

### TILIA, LINDEN, LIME

The linden has strong associations for persons of European background. It is a heavily foliaged tree, rounded and neat-looking, and splendid for shade. The fragrance of a linden in bloom is unforgettable. The European forms are generally considered superior to native and Asiatic kinds.

The little-leaf linden *(Tilia cordata)*, extremely hardy, adapts well to poor soil and city conditions. A native of Europe and usually seen as a small to medium-sized tree.

The silver linden *(Tilia tomentosa)*,* white undersides to the leaves, less hardy than the little-leaf linden. Has a reputation for tolerating heat and drought better than other lindens.

### ULMUS, ELM

The magnificent, vase-shaped American elm, as well as most other species of elm, are susceptible to the Dutch elm disease, which has taken a tremendous toll of specimens in various parts of the country and makes the planting of all but resistant varieties a most unwise venture. The two following are resistant:

The Christine Buisman elm (a variety of *Ulmus carpinifolia*), a handsome, broadly pyramidal tree, with glossy foliage.

The Chinese (Siberian) elm *(Ulmus pumila),** with rather dense
growth and small leaves. Grown in tubs in cities in the Midwest
with outstanding success. Drought resistant.

B. TREES WITH FEW SIGNIFICANT VARIETIES AND
   GENERALLY LIMITED DISTRIBUTION

   * Drought Resistant.      ** Wet Ground.      † Shore.

### AILANTHUS,* TREE-OF-HEAVEN

There is only one species, *Ailanthus altissima,* sometimes listed as
*Ailanthus glandulosa,* but there is a red-fruited variety, *erythro-*
*carpa.* The species and variety have hybridized freely and the conspicuous fruits of the female tree vary from light green through
shades of rose and orange.

The tree grows rapidly in youth, and more slowly as it gets older.
It is a rigid, stick-like plant at first, but in age the branches may dip
and curve gracefully. The bark darkens with age and has been
likened to lizard skin. It may become a very large tree. The leaves
are drooping and frond-like.

The ailanthus has enormous powers of survival under adverse
conditions. Provided self-seeding is checked, it is a valuable plant
to produce quick temporary foliage in a large bare area that has
been bulldozed for building. It can be kept to any height, since it
will resprout from a bit of naked stem, and makes a hedge or screen
or fair-sized tree in an incredibly short time.

### ALBIZZIA, SILK TREE

The silk tree *(Albizzia julibrissin),* a medium-sized tree which produces clusters of flowers like little pink powder-puffs. Flowering
extends over a period of about a month, from June to July, or
July to August. The flowers are followed by long pods. The foliage, which appears late in spring, is light green and feathery and,
even in a smoky city, remains remarkably fresh and cool looking
throughout the season. Sometimes several trunks arise from the
base and produce a spreading tree, and sometimes the branches
are high on a single somewhat curving gray-white trunk, over
which the soft foliage makes a dome-like crown. The graceful
silhouette of a single-trunk specimen is most attractive. The
hardier variety *rosea* is grown as far north as Boston and is a
little smaller than the type. Its flowers are a deeper color.

### AMELANCHIER, SHADBLOW

The shadblow *(Amelanchier canadensis),* brings the woods into the garden in spring. The fruit attracts birds. It is quite adaptable, and has been grown successfully in shady city gardens. A tree of the East and parts of the Midwest, but not hardy in the coldest parts of the country.

### ARBUTUS, STRAWBERRY TREE, MADRONE

The strawberry tree *(Arbutus unedo)*, a handsome small evergreen tree or large shrub popular in gardens on the Pacific Coast. Leaves dark green, glossy and leathery. Bell-shaped white or pinkish blossoms, and showy round strawberry-colored fruits, are produced at the same time. Slow growing and is said to dislike alkaline soil.

### CARPINUS, IRONWOOD

The ironwood or American hornbeam *(Carpinus caroliniana)* should be grown more widely than it is for its picturesque quality. It has several smooth, dark, spreading trunks, with a peculiar sinewy quality, which make them look as though they had been formed in a mould. Grows very slowly, in sun or shade. Fall color good. Extremely hardy. May be hard to get.

### CASSIA, GOLDEN SHOWER SENNA

The golden shower senna *(Cassia fistula)*, a small tree from India with compound leaves and showy racemes of bright yellow flowers. Growth limited to the warmest sections of the country.

### CASUARINA, HORSETAIL TREE, SHE-OAK

Two species from Australia, *Casuarina equisetifolia* and *Casuarina stricta*, are used in southern Florida and California shore plantings for their soil tolerance and resistance to salt spray. In appearance resemble pines, and can be clipped for hedges. The Australian common name, she-oak, does not seem to be used in America. A third common name, suggested by the color of the wood, is beefwood.

### CELTIS,* HACKBERRY

The Chinese hackberry *(Celtis sinensis)*, a very useful shade tree in dry sections of California and the Southwest. The leaves are elm-like. The hackberry of the East is subject to witch-broom disease, which disfigures though it does not harm the tree.

## CERCIS, REDBUD, JUDAS TREE

The American redbud *(Cercis canadensis)*, is the hardiest of the species grown. An extremely graceful small tree or large shrub, with roundish, widely-spaced leaves and small purplish pink flowers. Quite adaptable and sometimes grown in city gardens in the East. Resembles the bauhinia grown in California and warm sections of the country, and has a similar place in gardens.

## DELONIX, FLAME TREE

The flame tree or royal poinciana *(Delonix regia)* from Madagascar is identified with the tropics and the Far East, but is thoroughly at home in southern Florida. Foliage is fern-like and very thick. The brilliant scarlet flowers are one of the sights of the far South. A much more spreading, voluptuous tree than another famous sub-tropical ornamental, the jacaranda, and more difficult to place in a garden. It is really a tree for parks and boulevards.

## ELAEAGNUS, RUSSIAN OLIVE

Russian olive *(Elaeagnus angustifolia)*, a shrubby tree, silvery gray, extremely hardy, and very adaptable. Valued greatly by city and shore gardeners.

## EUGENIA, BRUSH CHERRY

The brush cherry *(Eugenia paniculata australis)*, a popular ornamental in southern California and Florida. Foliage dense and glossy. Can be clipped to make a good hedge.

## GINKGO,* MAIDENHAIR TREE

Though eventually the gingko will attain an immense size, a half century or so may slip through its boughs before it assumes the full-bosomed grandeur of a mature tree. It is a solitary tree in the plant world, the only survivor of a family that was common in the Coal Age. When it is young its branches may shoot out in all directions, giving it an odd, ungainly and yet picturesque quality. Some one has described it as having, in youth, "the spiny back of the dragon and its scaly beauty." It does not strike everyone like this, however, and I once heard a lady, indignant that it had been planted on her street, call it "that arthritic stick." The leaves, which grow from little spurs, are like giant leaflets of the maidenhair fern. The spurs elongate with age and produce an interesting silhouette on an old tree in winter. The fall color is typically a clear golden amber, unsullied by speck or splash of any other hue.

The ginkgo is actually the oldest nut tree in existence, the word ginkgo being a Japanese corruption of a Chinese word meaning "silver nut." Ginkgo nuts are still used in Japanese cooking and eaten to aid digestion. The tree is dioecious, and the female, nut-producing kind is unpopular because of the odor of the decaying yellow fruits. Nursery trees are propagated vegetatively from male specimens.

It is difficult to assess the place of the ginkgo in landscape work; it is one of those odd trees. It is sometimes used very effectively in a modernistic planting; and it is a pregnant thought that the oldest tree in the world adapts itself admirably to plantings around glass skyscrapers.

### GLEDITSIA,* HONEY LOCUST

The development of thornless, sterile varieties of the honey locust (*Gleditsia triacanthos*), has removed two former objections to the tree—the presence of dangerous thorns, and of pods that were messy when they fell on lawns. The tree is single-trunked and high branching, with a good crown. It is not hardy in the coldest parts of the country. It adapts itself to difficult growing conditions, is used in cities, and is generally popular. It is a "safe" tree in landscape work. Horticultural forms are Shademaster and Imperial.

### GORDONIA, LOBLOLLY BAY

The loblolly bay (*Gordonia lasianthus*), a large tree of the South, popular for its handsome glossy foliage and its fragrant white flowers. The species *G. alatamaha*, a smaller tree or shrub with larger flowers, is hardier and sometimes found in the vicinity of New York City. This species is also known as franklinia; it is a precious plant.

### GREVILLEA,* SILKY OAK

The silky oak (*Grevillea robusta*), an Australian ornamental, totally unlike a true oak. The feathery leaves are white and silky on the undersides; the flowers are orange yellow. Valued in southern California for its ability to thrive in poor sandy soils and its resistance to drought. Said to stand temperatures of 25 degrees F. The branches tend to break in exposed situations. In its native habitat a big tree. Most American books list it as silk oak.

### HALESIA, SILVERBELL

The Carolina silverbell (*Halesia carolina*), smaller and hardier than the mountain silverbell *(Halesia monticola)*. The white, bell-shaped flowers make it a charming tree in mid-spring. It is easy to maintain.

## JACARANDA, JACARANDA

*Jacaranda acutifolia,* native of Brazil, an outstanding flowering ornamental for subtropical regions. Foliage light and fernlike; clusters of lavender-blue flowers in early summer abundant and conspicuous. An open tree, branching fairly high on the trunk. Tolerates a variety of growing conditions, including some frost.

## KOELREUTERIA,* GOLDENRAIN TREE, VARNISH TREE

The goldenrain tree *(Koelreuteria paniculata),* one of the most useful small ornamental trees. Hardy into Massachusetts and southern New York and thrives under adverse growing conditions, including drought. Has been said to have weak wood, but a specimen in an exposed situation in Easthampton, Long Island, has withstood two hurricanes. In California tends to be a more rounded, compact tree than in the East, where it is open and picturesquely irregular in outline. The dark green, compound leaves have considerable substance. Yellow flowers in June-July or even earlier, according to location, followed by bladder-like fruits which typically turn rust color and are striking when the sun catches them. Bark brownish, tinged with orange. Usually single-trunked. A very pretty tree beside a terrace on a small property.

## LABURNUM, LABURNUM

The Scotch laburnum *(Laburnum alpinum),* hardier than the Waterer laburnum, a hybrid form of the common laburnum. Neither will grow in the coldest sections of the country. A small, stiff tree, remarkable mainly for its long, drooping clusters of bright yellow flowers.

## LAGERSTROEMIA, CRAPE-MYRTLE

The crape-myrtle *(Lagerstroemia indica),* a small tree or large shrub, with decorative growth habit and crinkled flowers in shades of pinkish lavender and white, is one of the "type" trees of southern gardens. Has been known to grow in sheltered spots are far north as Long Island. Blooms over a long period and is relatively pest free. Requires care when moving.

## LAURUS, LAUREL, SWEET BAY

*Laurus nobilis,* the aromatic laurel or bay of ancient history. Splendid for shearing, and as a small shade tree. Not hardy in the North, but can be grown in the South and many parts of the Pacific Coast. A tree for a manicured garden.

## LIQUIDAMBAR, SWEET GUM

The sweet gum *(Liquidambar styraciflua),* a large tree, handsome and individual. Dense, deeply-cut foliage is scarlet in fall. A native of the East, not hardy in the coldest sections of the country.

## LIRIODODENDRON, TULIP TREE

The tulip tree *(Liriododendron tulipifera),* a solitary and unique species. An immense tree in maturity, but branches high on a long straight trunk and a splendid tree to plant fairly close to a house, where the canopy shades the roof and there are no lower branches to present a problem. Seeds itself freely; the young seedlings are easily moved and grow quickly. Gets its common name from the greenish-yellow, quite large, tulip-shaped flowers, which always seem odd on such a big tree. In areas where young specimens are easy to get, it would be a splendid tree to use freely in a new housing development, where it would in a short time bestow a distinctive character. A native tree of the East, its natural habitat ranges into Massachusetts.

## MYRICA,** WAX MYRTLE, BAYBERRY

The California bayberry or Pacific wax myrtle *(Myrica californica),* a lustrous evergreen small tree or large shrub, much valued on the Pacific Coast. Useful for bogs and sandy soil.

## NYSSA,** SOUR GUM, BLACK GUM, TUPELO

The sour gum *(Nyssa sylvatica),* one of the truly distinctive native trees, with a wide range over the eastern United States. Leaves glossy and leathery and turn a brilliant color in early fall. Common in marshy land around Cape Cod. Not easy to transplant.

## OXYDENDRUM, SORREL TREE

The sorrel tree or sourwood *(Oxydendrum arboreum),* a superior ornamental in the East and on the Pacific Coast. Glossy green leaves turn scarlet and purplish in fall. Variously stated by an eastern horticulturist to have a maximum height of 75 feet, and by an Oregon authority to reach a height of 30 feet.

## PAULOWNIA, ROYAL PAULOWNIA

The royal paulownia or empress tree *(Paulownia tomentosa)* of China, a quick-growing, exotic looking tree with large coarse leaves and fragrant, violet-colored flowers. Hardy along the East Coast into the vicinity of Boston and New York. A rounded tree, of medium size at maturity, and useful in certain situations where a bold effect is needed.

## PHELLODENDRON, CORK TREE

The cork trees *(Phellodendron amurense* and *Phellodendron chinense)*, extremely hardy small to medium trees, quick growing when young, shapely when mature, at home in almost any kind of soil.

## PISTACIA,* PISTACHE

The Chinese pistache *(Pistacia chinensis)*, not the edible pistachio of commerce, but considered a useful shade tree in Florida, and in California at least as far north as Sacramento. Withstands heat and drought. Near Sacramento, it grows rapidly; in other locations is said to grow slowly. The foliage, which somewhat resembles that of a black walnut, may color bronze and red in fall. The young fruits are jade green, and very pretty on their bright red stalks. A charming tree, and may grow quite large.

## PLUMERIA, FRANGIPANI, TEMPLE TREE, PAGODA TREE

The exotic, heavily-perfumed tree of the tropics, inextricably linked in the minds of travelers with the temples of the East. Stripped of leaves, the stiff fleshy branches are grotesquely picturesque. The clusters of flowers are creamy yellow or pinkish purple. Two species grown in Florida, one known as the pagoda tree and the other as red jasmine. Frangipani should have a place to itself in any garden in which it can be grown.

## PONCIRUS, HARDY ORANGE

The hardy orange *(Poncirus trifoliata)*, an extremely ornamental small tree or large shrub, dependably hardy south of Philadelphia and grown much farther north in sheltered locations. The leaves not like orange leaves, but small and in three parts. Small white fragrant blossoms. Spreading, picturesque growth, fruit like small green velvet balls when young and orange-colored at maturity. Easy to grow from seed. Very thorny and makes an excellent compact clipped hedge. A plant of character and should be better known by owners of small gardens.

### ROBINIA,* BLACK LOCUST

The black locust (*Robinia pseudoacacia*), a tremendously hardy and adaptable tree of great character, with an irregular, picturesque quality in age. Except in extreme youth, not a spreading tree, and gets narrower with age. Drooping clusters of white, pea-like flowers in early summer are fragrant. Several varieties, one with rose-colored flowers that is smaller than the type. The bark of an old tree is deeply grooved in a diamond pattern.

The black locust grows rapidly and spreads by underground stems. It is light and graceful in youth, and another splendid tree for quick beautification of new, bare housing developments. When planted in boxes inside a city front fence, its growth is restrained and it makes an excellent lacy hedge. Grown in this way, it will stand almost unlimited abuse and drought.

### SCHINUS,* PEPPER TREE

The California pepper tree (*Schinus molle*), actually a native of Peru, and grows in many places besides California. A highly individual tree, with a sturdy, rugged character, and drooping branches clothed with light green, rather delicate foliage. The clusters of small, glistening, pinkish-rose berries are so abundant that sometimes a tree appears to be literally encrusted with fruit. The dropping of fruit and leaves makes it a messy tree for a lawn, but it is excellent on a gravel surface. Withstands drought and poor soils. Not a tree for a lush garden, but splendid for a desert type planting, where the pattern of the branches is effective on baked surfaces and bare walls. A tree for hot, dry sections.

Another species, *Schinus terebinthifolius*, the Brazil pepper tree, with bright red berries, is cultivated in Florida.

### SOPHORA,† SCHOLAR TREE, PAGODA TREE

The Japanese pagoda tree (*Sophora japonica*), a large spreading tree at maturity, with many excellent qualities. In the North, where it is hardy into coastal New England, it is among the last of the deciduous trees to lose its leaves in fall; I have seen it green in November when surrounding planes, ginkgos, tulip trees and elms were bare. Flowers in midsummer, producing clusters of creamy-white, pealike blossoms. Adapts excellently to city conditions. What is probably one of the biggest specimens in the country grows close to the shore in Massachusetts. A big tree usually seeds itself freely, and seedlings a few inches high will transplant readily and grow rapidly. Planted in boxes, and trimmed, they make a good hedge for city dwellers.

### STYRAX, SNOWBELL

The Japanese snowbell *(Styrax japonica)*, a large shrub, or small tree, rather spreading, with small, white, bell-shaped flowers in about June. A pretty thing for a fine planting, and hardy into coastal Massachusetts.

### UMBELLULARIA, CALIFORNIA LAUREL, SPICE TREE, BAY TREE

An aromatic evergreen, medium-sized tree native to the Pacific Coast.

### ZELKOVA SERRATA, ZELKOVA

This member of the elm family is resistant to the Dutch elm disease and is becoming increasingly popular as a substitute for the American elm. It grows rapidly, has a nice shape and attractive bark. The leaves turn russet in fall.

TREES USEFUL FOR HEDGES

*Non-cone-bearing:*
  Beech *(Fagus)* . . . List A.
  Black locust *(Robinia)* . . . List B.
  Brush cherry *(Eugenia)* . . . List B.
  Cockspur thorn *(Crataegus)* . . . List A.
  Hardy orange *(Poncirus)* . . . List B.
  Hedge or field maple *(Acer)* . . . List A.
  Holly *(Ilex)* . . . List A.
  Horsetail tree *(Casuarina)* . . . List B.
  Laurel *(Laurus)* . . . List B.
  Russian olive *(Elaeagnus)* . . . List B.
  Shingle oak *(Quercus)* . . . List A.

*Cone-bearing:*
  Douglas fir *(Pseudotsuga)*
  Hemlock *(Tsuga)*

## Chapter III

# FRUIT AND NUT TREES

The United States is rich in fruit and nut trees that are both ornamental and useful. For a fruit enthusiast, a small orchard or nut grove is an interesting variation from a "standard" garden, and just as pretty.

In the colder parts of the country, the choice is wide—apples, pears, cherries, quinces, peaches, apricots and plums. Dwarf varieties of apples and pears, which come into bearing sooner than trees grown on standard seedling rootstock, lend themselves admirably to espalier treatment. They also make delightful little specimen trees in a small garden and in a herb garden.

Though the kaki, or Japanese and Chinese persimmon, is confined mostly to California and areas south of the Mason-Dixon Line, there are hardy varieties and its range could, and undoubtedly would, be extended if more people were familiar with it and knew that they could grow it. There are tall-growing and dwarf forms. The scarlet foliage of a variety with a tall straight trunk and a high crown was and probably still is an arresting autumn spectacle in the Western Hills outside Peking, where the winters are bitterly cold. An Asiatic persimmon would be a handsome and original addition to a northeastern garden.

For warm-climate gardens there are oranges, lemons, limes, grapefruit, figs, pomegranates, loquats and mangoes. Among oranges, the distinctive mandarin (tangerine) type should not be overlooked; it is a small tree, and the fruit is brilliant.

The pomegranate *(Punica granatum)*, with arching branches, shiny light green leaves, and orange-red flowers, is a handsome shrub even without the large, showy fruits. It has a pronounced oriental appearance.

The loquat *(Eriobotrya japonica)* is a handsome small tree which should be popular in small home gardens in the warmer parts of the country. It is well shaped, with large, dark, glossy leaves, and clusters of yellow fruit.

For a nut tree, there are the beautiful English or Persian walnut, hardy into parts of Pennsylvania; the pecan of the South; the shrub-like and thoroughly hardy filbert or hazelnut; and the almond, with its cloud of spring bloom.

The shapely little medlar tree *(Mespilus germanica)* is well known to Europeans and sometimes grown in "traditional" herb gardens. The fruit is picked after frost and stored until it blets (softens). The beach plum *(Prunus maritima)* is for shore gardens. The seagrape *(Coccolobis uvifera)* of Florida beaches is a striking large shrub or small tree; the bold, strong leaves are valuable in providing texture contrast in foliage. The strawberry guava *(Psidium cattleianum)*, which may be either a large shrub or a small tree, is extremely ornamental, with glossy leaves and bright small fruits.

## Chapter IV

# SHRUBS

It is not easy to define a shrub, because plants that are shrubs in a park become trees in a little garden. Shrubs, like trees, can be single-stemmed or multiple-stemmed, and altogether offer such an enormous variety of forms, sizes, textures and color that it is possible to plant an entire garden with shrubs and have a season-long parade of color from flower and fruits and foliage. A shrub garden requires thoughtful planning, but it is one of the easiest kinds of garden to maintain.

## Green Gardens

The green boxwood gardens of Williamsburg in Virginia are shrub gardens, and it would be hard to imagine any more beautiful planting. Boxwood gardens, however, take years to grow, are very expensive, and can only be made under climatic conditions which do not exist in many parts of the country.

The subtle quality of a boxwood garden, with its elusive but memorable odor (it is scarcely fragrance) cannot be duplicated, but its simplicity can. A similar type of green garden can be worked out, for instance, in varieties of Japanese holly (*Ilex crenata*). The boxleaf Japanese hollies (*Ilex crenata convexa* and *bullata*) have leaves that are reflexed and very glossy and make a good contrast to a variety such as *rotundifolia,* with much larger rounded leaves, or *microphylla,* with small, dark rather pointed leaves.

A green garden can also be developed with varieties of yew (*Taxus*), or by a judicious selection of needle-leaf evergreens— dark green, light green, gray green, blue green, and so on.

An all-green garden is usually improved if it is relieved by a piece of sculpture or other garden feature. Colored tile in the masonry of steps or walls is often effective. The color pattern of a garden of evergreens is muted, and an elaborate ornament is not out of place. In a rose garden, on the other hand, there is so much pattern in the color of the flowers that simple ornaments are best.

## Scale

In a mixed garden, shrubs are second only to trees in their contribution to the planting backbone. When a very large tree is growing in a small garden, the maxims about scale may require a second look; if the shrubs are in proportion to the tree, there won't be any room for the owners, and the garden, even as a spectacle to be viewed from indoors, will be crowded, with the identity of individual plants lost. A huge tree in a confined space is such a dominant feature that it is usually best to keep the rest of the planting low.

## Shrubs in the Flower Border

In a small garden, shrubs can be combined effectively with perennials, annuals and bulbs in a border. The shrubs may be used as backbone material, as occasional plants to strengthen the border, or as the main planting, with the smaller material planted in pockets in the foreground. The glossy abelia (*Abelia grandiflora*) and some of the shrubby cinquefoils (*Potentilla*), such as Katherine Dykes, with primrose-colored flowers, and Gold Drop (bright yellow) are especially useful for combining with flowers. Daphnes are also good.

Some deciduous shrubs are valuable for the color of their stems in winter. The stems of the red-osier dogwood (*Cornus stolonifera*) are so brilliant that they look artificial; they are effective at a distance but are too overpowering for a close view. There is also a yellow-stemmed variety.

## Fragrant Shrubs

A number of shrubs are extremely fragrant, and since shrubs are nearer the ground than trees, and larger than sweet-smelling annuals and perennials, one fragrant shrub can usually do more to perfume a garden than any other single plant. The scent of a sweet olive or a fragrant daphne can literally drench a garden.

### Selection of Shrubs

Choosing a shrub involves a less momentous decision than choosing a tree, because a shrub can be more easily replaced. Soil is not as crucial a consideration, not because a shrub is any less particular about the soil in which it grows, but because the soil for a shrub can be more easily controlled than that for a tree.

Exposure, on the other hand, is usually more important, because while a tree reaches up to the heavens, a shrub cannot get the light and air it needs unless it is properly placed.

### Needle-leaf Shrubs

Shrubs, like trees, fall into two big groups, needle-leaf (usually cone-bearing) and broad-leaf (non-cone-bearing). Needle-leaf shrubs are typically evergreen and are most important in cold-climate gardens, where, without them, the garden would be virtually bare for several months of the year. Their inability to thrive under sooty conditions creates one of the major problems in city gardening.

The needle-leaf class of evergreens is represented by comparatively few genera and species, but by a tremendous number of forms, so that any one kind may be available in dwarf, medium or large sizes, and stiffly upright, loosely spreading or prostrate shapes. They also present a large assortment of shades and intensities of green: dark green, light green, yellow green, gray green and blue green. The leaves can be spiky, flat, or plumy. The striking contrast in texture and color of an assortment of needle-leaf evergreens is difficult to appreciate even in a well-stocked nursery; the gardener wishing to evaluate this kind of material should study a planting in a botanical garden.

The yew and the juniper, two of the most popular needle-leaf evergreens, are not cone-bearing. They both bear extremely attractive fruit, bright red in the yew and blue-black in the juniper, but since they are dioecious, there will be no fruit unless a male and a female specimen are planted. This fact is not always mentioned in the captions of nursery catalog pictures of a handsomely fruited yew or juniper.

PRUNING NEEDLE-LEAF SHRUBS. If needle-leaf evergreens are cut back to old wood, the old wood will not produce new growth. Many kinds hold their shape naturally, but, when trimming is necessary, it should be done by shortening young growth. Yew is most likely to need trimming. This is the evergreen that was used for topiary work in old formal gardens of the classical style. It makes a handsome clipped hedge.

Yew is, in fact, the most flexible of the needle-leaf evergreens for garden work; some kinds, notably Hicks yew, can be espaliered.

The kinds of needle-leaf evergreen in common use as shrubs are yew *(Taxus)*, juniper *(Juniperus)*, arborvitae *(Thuja)*, and *Chamaecyparis*. Because of the many horticultural forms in each group, not all nurseries carry the same varieties. The gardener is better off when buying if he specifies a size, shape and color, rather than a named variety. The nursery may not have that variety in stock, but can often supply another that is similar.

General cultural advice is:

1. Never let needle-leaf evergreens go into the winter dry. Give a good soaking in late fall if the weather is dry, and if there is not much snow or rain during the winter, water on mild days.

2. When the air is polluted with soot, hose the foliage frequently.

3. Don't use peat moss when planting yew, unless lime is added. Yew does not like acid soil.

4. Junipers and arborvitae need sun.

5. Yew and hemlock do well in shade.

## Broad-leaf Shrubs (non-cone-bearing)

This group includes the broad-leafed evergreens of the North and the big group of shrubs that are deciduous in cold parts of the country and often evergreen in warmer sections.

I. EVERGREEN. The term broad-leaf evergreens is confusing to persons in warm climates, where almost everything is evergreen, but to those in areas where winter transforms many heavily foliaged plants into woody skeletons, broad-leafed evergreens are an enormously important group of plants. They include some of the richest material found in gardens—rhododendrons, azaleas, laurel, boxwood, holly, pieris, euonymus. These plants are mostly lovers of acid soil, and are the saving grace of many gardens in the big cities of the East and the Northeast, where the list of possible plant material is severely curtailed.

Rhododendrons and azaleas represent a huge group of species and varieties, native and foreign, which is being constantly enlarged and improved by artificial hybridization.

Botanically, both rhododendrons and azaleas are rhododendrons, but there is a big difference in the general appearance of the two groups. There are many kinds of rhododendrons, from tiny dwarf varieties to forms as big as trees, but by and large their characteristics are picturesque shape, an absence of twigginess, large, thick, dark green elliptical leaves, and a conspicuous terminal growth of pale overlapping scales. The flowers are commonly white, or shades of rose, rose purple and red.

The evergreen azaleas, on the other hand, are extremely twiggy; they are also more compact, and large plants give an impression of tiers of growth. The leaves are generally lighter in color, smaller, and more shiny than those of rhododendrons. The flowers, too, are smaller.

Nursery specimens of azaleas usually suggest a plant much more diminutive than a rhododendron, but some kinds may get very big and the gardener who wants his plant to remain dwarf should be sure that he is buying a dwarf form. He should also remember that deciduous azaleas are more common in general garden work than deciduous rhododendrons, and, if he wants an evergreen, to be sure that he gets a kind that will hold its leaves in winter.

Rhododendrons and azaleas both like a very acid soil, and it is common practice to mix them in a planting, but often they would look much better apart. In a small garden, a single azalea, suitably placed and near a contrasting texture such as gray stone, is often much more effective than a mass. Azaleas are used with consummate art in Japan, often being sheared into low mounded forms.

Laurel is one of those names that mean different plants in different places. The laurel of ancient history is a tree. The common laurel or laurel-cherry of the Pacific Coast is English laurel (*Prunus laurocerasus*), a tall, handsome shrub with large glossy leaves. The laurel of the East is mountain laurel or calico bush *(Kalmia latifolia)*, a highly distinctive plant with lovely cup-shaped flowers in white or shades of pink. It retains something of a wild look in cultivation, and is more in keeping with a naturalistic planting than either rhododendrons or azaleas. Its very name, calico bush, suggests this subtle distinction. It is a very beautiful plant indeed, with strong glossy leaves, and the unopened flower buds have a classc purity.

*Pieris japonica,* sometimes sold as andromeda or even simply as japonica, is usually a medium-sized shrub. It is much superior to the native species, which is the only other one offered. The drooping clusters of bell-like flowers come very early in spring. One of the most attractive features of the plant is the coral color of the young growth. Though pieris does well in shade, it shows to better advantage when it is brightened by a little sun. It is an exclusive-looking plant which should not be thrown in anyhow with a mass of other material.

The Japanese hollies *(Ilex crenata* in variety) are an immensely important group of evergreen foliage plants over big sections of the country. They do not in the least resemble Christmas holly. The dark green, shiny leaves are quite small and the berries are black. The chief difference among varieties is the ultimate size of the plant and a slight variation in leaf size. In the box-leaf holly *(Ilex crenata convexa)*, the leaf is reflexed in a way that makes the over-all foliage texture distinctive.

Japanese holly is widely used in northeastern city gardens and is extremely valuable and dependable for creating a rich, glossy, compact evergreen mass. An old specimen of *Ilex crenata microphylla,* in which the stems have thickened to small trunks and the leaves darkened, may bear a close resemblance to tree boxwood. This variety is exceptionally hardy.

The several varieties of evergreen euonymus are handsome plants with leathery, dark green, polished leaves. They are easy to grow, in either sun or shade. Some kinds have a half-trailing habit, and can be used as ground covers, trained against a wall, or grown as shrubs. *Euonymus japonicus* is perhaps the most beautiful, but it is not hardy in the North, where *Euonymus radicans vegetus* is a good substitute. *Euonymus patens,* half-evergreen in the North, thrusts long basal shoots into the bed, which root and form a ground cover. It is unusual in that it produces a cloud of small white flowers in late summer. Euonymus varieties are invaluable in city gardens, since the sheen on the leaves is not dulled by smoke and soot.

## II. DECIDUOUS

The deciduous shrubs class is the most difficult in which to choose a few plants. It is an immense group, and though it includes many plants that are distinctive at every season of the year, it also includes material that is nondescript except during a brief blooming period. Shrubs in this category are always pictured in full bloom, and it is easy to be carried away by this gorgeous display of color photography. Some, such as mock-orange, weigela, beauty bush, forsythia, some kinds of spirea, and bush honeysuckles, grow very large. They are excellent for screening, but the gardener should beware of using them so liberally in a small garden that the planting is without character during most of the year.

### Pruning for Shape

Certain shrubs in this group lend themselves admirably to espalier work, and to other forms of drastic treatment with the pruning shears. It is a general horticultural principle that the pruning of a deciduous shrub should preserve its natural shape. This is a valid rule when the natural shape is picturesque and the natural growth restrained, as in the lovely manzanita of California (*Arctostaphylos stanfordiana*), the black haw (*Viburnum prunifolium*), the dwarf Japanese flowering quince (*Chaenomeles japonica*), the fragrant *Viburnum carlesi*, and the beach plum (*Prunus maritima*). When, however, the garden is small and the natural growth of a shrub suggests a pile of green hay, the gardener is justified in cutting ruthlessly to obtain a shape that pleases him and fits into his planting scheme. (In doing so, remember that spring-flowering shrubs should be pruned *after* flowering, so that growth may be produced for next year's bloom. Prune fall-flowering shrubs in spring, for flowers on the current season's growth.)

Forsythia is much more effective trained in a fan shape against a wall than left as a loose, floppy bush. Mock orange and weigela are also good espalier subjects. An old honeysuckle can be trimmed to give value to the stem. An ancient California privet, with a thickened trunk, can be shaped into a prim little tree, with a rounded or cone-shaped head.

## Colored Fruits

The fruits of some shrubs are much more showy than the flowers. Since fruits usually hang on the bushes longer than flowers, shrubs grown for their fruit may ensure a longer display than if grown for flowers. Shrubs with handsome fruits are the snowberry and the waxberry (*Symphoricarpos*), several species of bush honeysuckle (*Lonicera*), the cranberry-bush (*Viburnum trilobum*), the orange-fruited tea viburnum (*Viburnum setigerum aurantiacum*), the linden viburnum (*Viburnum dilatatum*), jetbead (*Rhodotypos tetrapetala*), cotoneasters in variety, pyracantha, several species of euonymus, and the Japanese barberry (*Berberis thunbergi*).

When there is an even choice between two flowering shrubs, check the fruiting habit; the fruits of one may be insignificant and of the other ornamental.

## Shrubs with Tradition

Many deciduous shrubs are identified so closely with certain parts of the country and certain types of garden that they carry an aura of association and tradition. Lilacs, for instance, have gladdened New Englanders for so many generations that it is difficult to think of a New England garden of high or low degree without a lilac. The aromatic calycanthus, known variously as sweet-scented shrub, sweet shrub, strawberry shrub, and even just "shrub," is often familiar to older people who may not know the name of any other plant, and it carries with it the association of many an old-fashioned dooryard plot and many a childhood memory.

The sweet-olive (*Osmanthus fragrans*) and the crape-myrtle (*Lagerstroemia indica*) inevitably conjure up pictures of languorous summer evenings in the rich old gardens of the South. The crape-myrtle is totally different from the true myrtle (*Myrtus communis*), a smaller shrub with scented leaves and flowers and handsome purplish fruits. The true myrtle is ever-blooming in southern California, and spring flowering farther north. It is sometimes used for hedges. The word myrtle has been accumulating associations since the time of ancient Greece and has been bestowed somewhat indiscriminately on a number of plants, probably by persons enamored of its poetic connotation.

*Roses as Shrubs*

Roses are too often overlooked when choosing a shrub. Some of the old-fashioned species and hybrids grow very large and are excellent shrub material. They leaf out very early in spring, and the colored hips of many kinds are extremely decorative in later summer and fall. Shrub roses are discussed in the section on roses.

## Tropical and Subtropical Shrubs

In southern Florida, and parts of southern California and the Gulf Coast, hibiscus in gorgeous colors, oleanders, and shrub forms of allamanda and bougainvillaea are type plants; they are so vivid and invidual that they create a garden style of their own. The sort of delicate ground embroidery that is appropriate and charming in a northern garden becomes unthinkable in association with such violent pigments. They are a subject in themselves, and cannot possibly receive any kind of justice in a book of this size. Indeed, the number of beautiful shrubs from which the average gardener is free to choose all over the country is so great that it has not been possible to do more than skim the surface of their usefulness.

## Chapter V

# *VINES*

Failure to appreciate the ornamental value of vines, and their enormous diversity, makes them too often the stepchildren of a garden. It is true that all vines climb, but apart from this common feature they differ more from each other than any other class of plants.

A vine may live for a hundred years or more, or need to be renewed annually from seed. It may develop a trunk as thick as a tree, or be a slender, spineless plant. It may attach itself to a wall by aerial roots or little disks, or require a support. It may twine round the support, clockwise or counter-clockwise according to its mysterious habit; or it may have to be tied. It may be perennial, but die to the ground every year in cold climates. It may be evergreen or deciduous. It may be notable for its flowers, fruits, fall color, fragrance, or simply for its fresh green leaves. It may be a strong, smothering plant; or trace a delicate pattern on a wall. It may bear murderous spines; or have stems as clean as a whistle. It may be brittle and easily broken; or produce yards of stem with the strength and flexibility of rope. In short, a vine is a many-featured thing, much less uniform in its behavior than a shrub or a tree, both of which are consistently woody and relatively permanent.

It will be seen, therefore, that anyone who "just plants a vine" may not at all achieve what he wants. When choosing a vine, its purpose should be very clear. Is it, for instance, to shade a porch or arbor, to clothe an unsightly structure, to provide a quick screen, to scramble over a wall or fence, to serve as a ground cover, or to adorn the face of a building?

## Planting

Perennial vines, including woody ones, are generally set out as small plants. It is easy to forget the size they will attain, and the root system required to support a large permanent vine. Soil preparation should not be confined to a few inches around the roots, but should be proportionate to the size and longevity of the vine. Soil for most strong-growing woody vines should be deep and extend for several feet laterally. The exception is when the vine tends to be too rank a grower and it is wished to restrain it.

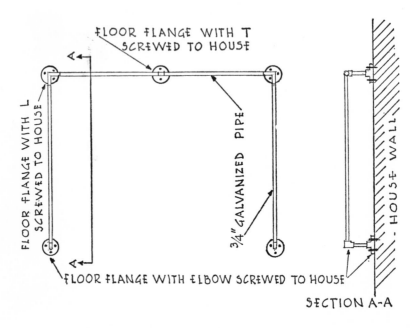

NOTE: SCREW PIPES TO ELBOWS, T's & L's
REMOVE FOR PAINTING

Fig. 58. From the office of Mary Deputy Cattell, Landscape Architect. A support for heavy twisting vines, such as actinidia, bittersweet, Dutchman's pipe, kudzu vine, wistaria.

## Vine Supports

Vines lacking appendages to anchor them to a wall must be provided with supports.

1. HEAVY TWISTING VINES. Figure 58 shows a support for a heavy twisting or twining vine, such as wistaria, bittersweet,

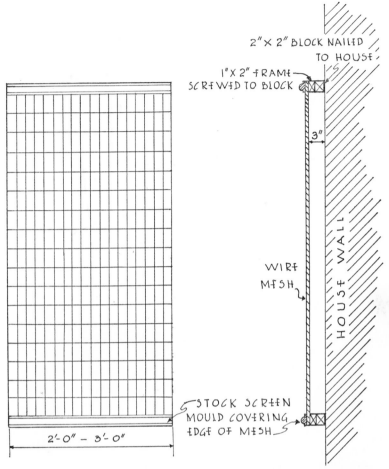

2"× 2" BLOCK NAILED
TO HOUSE

1"× 2" FRAME
SCREWED TO BLOCK

3"

WIRE
MESH

HOUSE WALL

STOCK SCREEN
MOULD COVERING
EDGE OF MESH

2'-0" – 3'-0"

Fig. 59. From the office of Mary Deputy Cattell, Landscape Architect. Support for a tendril vine, such as clematis, cobaea, passion-flower, sweet pea.

Dutchman's pipe, certain honeysuckles, kudzu vine and actinidia. The height and width of the support varies, of course, with the amount of wall surface it is desired to cover. It will be observed that the support stands out from the wall. The space to allow between wall and support depends on the type of vine; it should not be less than three inches.

Another method of supporting this type of vine is to use stranded copper wire cable. This is an excellent method when the vine is to be trained up the front of a house to a height of more than one story. Strong projecting wire hooks are inserted

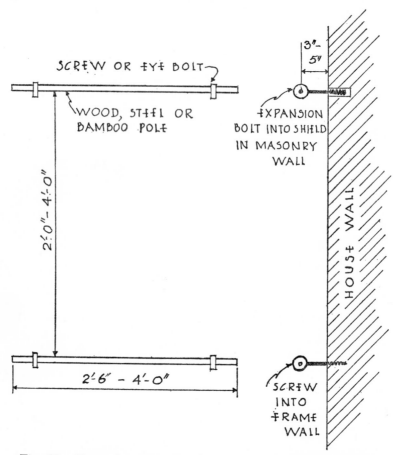

Fig. 60. From the office of Mary Deputy Cattell, Landscape Architect. Support for an espaliered vine or shrub or climbing rose.

in the masonry at the height to which the vine is to be trained and the cable secured to the hooks. The hooks should project a few inches from the wall.

A familiar sight to New Yorkers is a fleece vine or a wistaria trained in a single rope up the face of a building, so that it presents the appearance in summer of a great green feather boa. A more interesting pattern can be obtained, especially on a low wide building, where it is desired to cover a large surface, by hanging several vertical cables and connecting them by cross pieces. A rapid-growing vine, such as fleece vine, Dutchman's pipe, or kudzu, will cover a scaffolding of this sort in a very short time.

*Photograph by Gottscho-Schleisner, Inc.*

Plate 24. A graceful white fence bridges the gap between a neighboring house and a high wall screening the entrance to the owner's residence. The fence also provides a background for the irregular beds of low-growing flowers which give a welcoming charm to the approach. The lilac at the far end and the pyracantha near the door help to define the garden and make a transition from the heavy planting outside to the almost cottage garden effect in the immediate foreground. Bulbs planted in fall for spring flowering, and annuals planted in spring, would give season-long color in the beds with very little maintenance.

*Robert Zion and Harold Breen, Site Planners and Landscape Architects, New York, N. Y.; photographs by Alexandre Georges; reproduced by permission of McCall's*

Plate 25.   The square-cut flagstone paving of this 19′ x 39′ terrace is laid on a 4″ bed of sand, with sand swept over the top to fill the cracks. A wood or metal curb may be used to define the edge of the terrace. A 5′ framing fence forms an L along two sides. Sword ferns fill the generous square planting pocket at the base of an old apple tree. (A good method for deciding on the exact limits of such a terrace would be to test dimensions by hanging sheets between rough supporting posts.)

Plate 26, opposite:   Another view of the same terrace shows it in relationship to the kitchen door.

*Photograph by J. Horace McFarland Company*

Plate 27.　An ornamental gate bestows grace on this garden entrance. White paint on the pillars and ceiling of the wistaria-covered porch lighten the area.

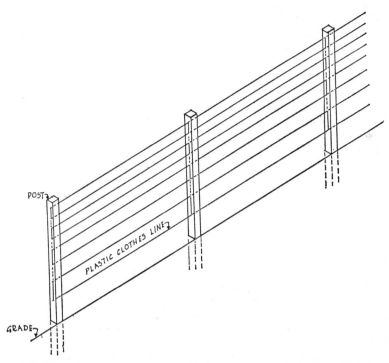

POST

PLASTIC CLOTHES LINE

GRADE

Fig. 61. From the office of Roberta Lord, Landscape Architect. A support for annual or other short-lived vines planted as a screen. This would be a useful support for such vines as morning glory, moonflower, scarlet runner bean, passion-flower and sweet pea.

Stranded copper wire is sold by weight, and is graded according to the number of wires in a strand and the gauge of the wire. Some cables are very fine. A cable between one-quarter and one-half inch thick will support a heavy vine. There are approximately twelve feet in a pound of quarter-inch cable.

2. TENDRIL VINES. Figure 59 shows a support for tendril vines. These are best trained on a structure with horizontal and vertical pieces, such as lattice work or wire mesh. Chicken wire deteriorates rapidly; general-purpose galvanized welded wire mesh is much more durable. Coarse and fine meshes are available; the coarser the mesh the lower the price.

Grape vines, cobaea, passion vines, clematis and sweet peas are well known vines climbing by means of tendrils.

3. ESPALIERED VINES. Figure 60 shows a simple support for a

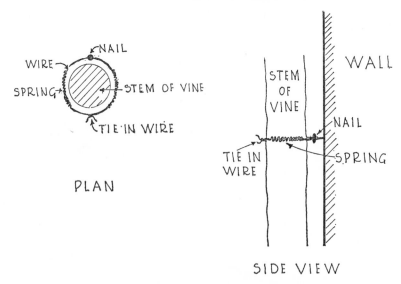

PLAN

SIDE VIEW

Fig. 62.   This method of tying vines was devised by Mr. Louis P. Politi, Horticulturist at The New York Botanical Garden, to prevent girdling of a strong woody vine when the stem thickens and the wire holding it in position becomes tight and cuts into the bark. Mr. Politi makes a spring in the wire by twisting it around a pencil. As the vine grows, the spring unwinds and there is no injurious pressure on the stem. Copper wire is best.

vine or other type of plant that is to be espaliered. It is also excellent for a hybrid perpetual or climbing rose. Hooks and wire cable may be substituted for the poles and bolts.

All these supports can be detached, with the vine, when the wall needs painting.

4. SHORT-LIVED VINES.   Figure 61 shows a useful support for annual or other short-lived vines planted as a screen. Green plastic-covered clothes-line is threaded through holes in the wooden posts. The better grade of clothesline, in which fine wire forms the core of the line, does not stretch as much as the grade in which twine is the core. Thread each panel separately; this will make a tighter support. It will also be easier to repair the fence if there is a break. For a heavy, permanent vine, the plastic might not be sufficiently rigid.

**Patterns with Vines**

Both plastic clothesline and stranded copper are excellent

for threading through screw eyes to a wall or fence to make an interesting pattern. In this way a vine can be trained in a number of designs, symmetrical and asymmetrical. It sometimes happens that windows are awkwardly placed, and the wall presents badly proportioned areas. A vine tracery can often be designed to beautify such a wall. Plate 1, following page 32, shows how a design in ivy can be used not only to decorate a wall but to help contain an area visually.

## Self-supporting Vines

Certain valuable vines, including English ivy *(Hedera)*, Boston ivy *(Parthenocissus)*, wintercreeper *(Euonymus)*, climbing hydrangea *(Hydrangea)*, Japanese hydrangea vine *(Schizophragma)*, and creeping fig *(Ficus)* are supplied with appendages to hold them fast to a wall. These vines should not be used on a wooden wall, since they cannot be easily removed for painting; moreover they may damage the wood. They are excellent for masonry walls. The English ivy, which climbs by rootlets, is more dependent on a rather rough surface than Boston ivy, which is equipped with little sticky disks at the ends of branched tendrils and seems able to cling to anything. For this reason, it may be troublesome to get English ivy started up a new wall, though roughening the mortar in places may help.

## Wall Blankets

ENGLISH AND BOSTON IVY. In the group of self-supporting vines, three kinds, two of which are evergreen and one deciduous, serve a unique purpose. They are English ivy *(Hedera helix)*, creeping fig *(Ficus pumila* or *F. repens)*, and Boston ivy *(Parthenocissus tricuspidata)*.

English ivy in the North, and creeping fig in the South, perform a similar function of clothing immense areas of masonry with an evergreen blanket. This is, literally, a blanket, because it has been proved that buildings covered with English ivy are warmer in winter and remain in a better state of preservation than buildings that are exposed. In hot weather, a protective covering of ivy or creeping fig helps to keep a building cool.

As one travels north of New York, English ivy becomes uncertainly hardy. The Baltic variety *(Hedera helix baltica)* is hardier, but in very cold parts of the country it is not wise to plant any variety of English ivy in a sunny winter exposure, particularly a southwest exposure; loss of water from the leaves when the ground is frozen and water cannot be replaced may cause the foliage to burn.

Boston ivy, which is neither a true ivy nor a native of Boston, is the other major self-supporting vine used for clothing masonry walls in the North. It is deciduous, but the branching stems in time makes a dense mat. It is much faster growing than English ivy; a vine may reach a height of three stories in as many years. It is also hardier.

The fall color of Boston ivy is typically brilliant, and if English ivy and Boston ivy are planted against the same wall the combination is most pleasing. In fall, the dark green ivy sets off the red of the deciduous vine. In winter, the wall is patterned with a tracery of bare stems and irregular masses of the cold-darkened ivy leaves. Snow is caught and held briefly against the wall.

Two varieties of Boston ivy common in the trade are Low's Japanese creeper *(Parthenocissus tricuspidata lowi)* and Veitch's Japanese creeper *(Parthenocissus tricuspidata veitchi).* All three kinds are often sold simply as Boston ivy, though the differences among them are important. The varieties are less vigorous than the type, and though Veitch's creeper will make good progress on a high wall, Low's creeper should be planted only where a delicate tracery on a low wall is required.

These two plants, English ivy and Boston ivy, have been discussed in some detail, because they serve a unique purpose and there is a great deal of misunderstanding about them. It is unfortunate that Boston ivy was ever so named, since this has led to a popular impression that some ivies are deciduous. *All true ivies are evergreen.*

CREEPING FIG. The creeping fig *(Ficus pumila)* grows, unfortunately, only in the far South. It is an exceedingly handsome vine, more close-knit than English ivy, so that it literally encrusts a wall with a dense mesh of stems. The young growth is fine-textured, but the old growth is coarse and requires pruning to keep it within bounds.

## Annual Vines

Annual vines are of great value in new gardens because of their quick growth and often handsome display of bright-colored flowers. They also give a new gardener an opportunity to discover, with a minimum of expense and effort, the effect of vines in different places, and the color that is most pleasing. Often one does not know, until one sees it, just how successful a flare of red or a dash of bright blue may be in a particular spot. With a ball of soft twine or a length of clothesline and some screw eyes, he can experiment with trellis designs—perhaps frame a window, or design a vertical panel, or test a horizontal treatment. When it is not desired to insert permanent eyes into a wall for a temporary job, attachments sold by garden supply stores can be used.

Anyone embarking on a project with annual vines is advised to study a seed catalog and follow his fancy. The choice offered, especially in the South, is wide and varied.

The gardener should remember that even annual vines can be quite temperamental in their needs, and he cannot know what to expect until he tries. The morning glory (*Ipomoea purpurea*) is an example. Anyone who has seen this vine growing lustily, reseeding itself, and mounting a cord to the height of a second story from a foothold of sooty soil a few inches deep in New York City might reasonably assume that morning glory would grow anywhere. He has only to go to Connecticut or upstate New York, however, to find a garden where the owner is sadly cherishing a stunted and almost sterile vine. He may travel up the street, or on to the nearby Berkshire Hills in Massachusetts and find morning glories performing in a way unsurpassed in their native Mexico.

## Vine Varieties

Some of the most spectacular flowers and fruits in the garden world are produced on vines. It is almost impossible to make a selection of "best" vines, because they grow in so many different ways that the manner of growth may disqualify for a particular situation a long list of excellent vines. In choosing a vine, the immediate background of a fence or wall is often more important than it is for a free-standing plant.

Fig. 63.    Wistaria can be grown as a shrub. In time, with careful pruning, it acquires a shape that is especially decorative in winter.

Those who have nostalgic memories of fragrant jasmine or stephanotis, or have been dazzled by bougainvillaea or allamanda, or fascinated by the curious formation of the passion vine, or found themselves spellbound before great purple blooms of clematis, or gladdened by the orange fruits of bittersweet, need no reminder. They only want to find out whether *that* is the vine they can grow.

Any fairly comprehensive vine list includes at least a hundred and probably nearer two hundred varieties, many of them well known. *The Handbook of Vines,* published by the Brooklyn Botanic Garden, describes vines for every section of the country, classifying them in a number of helpful ways, including rate and method of growth, flower and fruiting habits, preference as to moisture, dry soil, sun and shade. The reader is advised to study this or a similar text, a number of which exist.

## Chapter VI

# GROUND COVERS

## Lawns

The northern gardener tends to think of a lawn as an essential part of a garden. It is more usual for him to ask "Where shall I put the lawn?" than to ponder whether he wants a lawn at all as part of his design. He forgets that in hot dry climates a lawn may not be possible and that a fine garden can be made without one.

There is no question about the beauty of a well-kept lawn. Nor is there any question that it increases maintenance and that many home owners give more time to the lawn than to any other part of the garden. It is therefore important for anyone planning a garden to review his attitude towards them.

The closely mown grass of a lawn is a ground cover, but a ground cover in a class of its own. The plant that comes closest to a substitute for the grasses of a lawn is probably dichondra. This is widely used in California in sunny well-drained locations and is mown by some owners in the same way as grass. With, however, the possible exception of dichondra, closely mown grass reveals the modeling of the surface it covers in a way that other ground covers do not. This is, of course, most striking in a large area, but even in a small lawn one can be reminded of the flow and rhythm of the earth's crust. To aim for the flatness of a billiard table and slice off every little bump in the natural contouring makes for dullness.

A lawn that is depressed a little in the center will make an area look larger; one that is slightly convex will decrease the apparent size. In flat country, a gentle slope looks steeper than it does in hilly land; this device can be used to give topographical interest to one's yard. Conversely, in hilly country a rather flat lawn will look flatter and this again may be an effect you want to achieve.

The shadows cast on a lawn by the trunks and branches of a tree, and by clouds passing overhead, enhance the beauty and interest of a garden. It is pleasing to look across a lawn to a flower or shrub border. A lawn may also be a foreground for a distant object beyond the confines of the garden. I recall a garden in the lovely little town of Provo in Utah where one looked across a sweep of lawn to a snow-capped peak of the Rockies.

Many people, especially those who are country-bred, derive pleasure from arising in the morning to a lawn made silvery by dew. Most people enjoy the feeling of springy turf underfoot, and there is no cleaner, safer surface for little children to play on.

TEXTURE IN LAWNS.   Lawn purists like to grow grasses that produce a lawn as nearly as possible uniform in color and texture. Others prefer a pattern of light and dark green and coarse and fine texture. White or Dutch clover is deliberately planted in some lawns to produce areas that are lighter in color and of a different texture from grass. The critics of clover in a lawn object that it is more slippery than grass and is brown all winter.

FLOWERS IN LAWNS.   A lawn may be embroidered with small flowers, such as English daisies *(Bellis perennis)*. Some heads will be chopped off by the mower, but there will be blooms between mowings.

Meadow saffron, commonly called autumn crocus (*Colchicum* in variety), planted in late summer, will flower in September and October. The leaves appear the following spring, but die down during the summer, and the white and lilac flowers spring up in the grass again in the fall. There are also autumn-flowering varieties of the true crocus that may be used in the same way. Since meadow saffron and crocuses are bulbs, the foliage should not be cut; it is therefore advisable to plant them at the edge of the lawn, and keep the mower away from them.

MAKING A LAWN.   Such enormous energy has been concentrated on the anti-crabgrass campaign, and so much sales literature is obsessed with weed control, that there is a tendency for the lawns of America to be presented rather as battlegrounds than as areas of restful green. While it is true that crabgrass in a northern lawn will be brown from fall until early summer, it is perfectly practicable for a summer place and makes a rather nice-textured light green mat. In southern Florida I have seen it carefully tended. As for the other lawn weeds, the gardener must decide for himself whether his approach shall be that of a crusader or whether he prefers to take a few in his stride. A pretty little flower called bluets *(Houstonia coerulea)* is technically a weed in lawns, but it possesses considerable charm for those who are not purists.

A good lawn cannot be made by simply scattering grass seed in the chosen area. The soil must be fertile and easily worked to a depth of at least six or eight inches; deep soil encourages strong roots and vigorous plants, and is just as important for lawns made by laying strips of sod as for grass grown from seed. Drainage must be good. Sunlight must be adequate. Sufficient moisture must be available.

The kinds of grass to grow vary in different parts of the country. A mixture of several kinds of grass is usually preferred to a single variety. This is to insure survival if one kind does not take hold or falls victim to pest injury. Grass seed companies make up mixtures for different types of lawn—rough play lawns, medium use lawns, and fine picture lawns. Mixtures are also available for dry and moist areas, and for sun and shade.

A discussion of the respective merits of the different kinds of grass and of the steps to be followed in making a lawn are beyond the scope of this book, which is primarily an introduction to garden thinking. T. H. Everett's *Lawns and Landscaping Handbook* is excellent for lawn makers throughout the United States.

LAWN EDGINGS. When a lawn adjoins flower borders, use an edging to keep grass out of the beds. If brick is used, lay the bricks flush with the lawn to permit easy mowing. Pack the bricks as tight as possible, to prevent grass from getting between them.

Green plastic edgings are inexpensive and inconspicuous. Steel edgings, sunk into the ground until the top is flush with the grass and secured with metal stakes, have been known to last for many years.

The type of curb to use depends a good deal on the type of

planting in the bed. If the edges of the bed are to be exposed for even part of the year, the edging should be treated as a finish and a decoration.

A SUNKEN LAWN.   A lawn sunk about a foot below the level of the surrounding garden, and planted along the sloping sides with an evergreen ground cover, can be very effective. This treatment is particularly successful if the lawn is in the form of a panel or oval. English ivy and the less rampant Baltic ivy are good plants for a low bank bordering a lawn. A variety with the cumbersome name of ivy 238th Street (because it was discovered as a sport at this location in New York City) has flatter sprays than either of the above two varieties and hugs the ground more closely. Wintercreeper would also be suitable for such a bank, or a mat-like gray-green juniper such as the variety Bar Harbor.

EXTENDING THE LAWN WITH GROUND COVERS.   A very pretty tapestry border to a lawn may be made by planting low or mat-like ground covers around the edge, so that the grass flows into them, or they into the grass. Strong-growing kinds will compete with the grass and will not be hurt by a trimming from the mower. This treatment is especially satisfactory in small dished lawns in a tiny garden.

By alternating evergreen and deciduous plants, the picture is carried into winter. Small bulbs such as crocus, glory of the snow *(Chinodoxa)*, grape hyacinth *(Muscari)*, squill *(Scilla)* and the Lebanon squill *(Puschkinia)*, planted in fall among the deciduous plants, make a charming picture in early spring. Suitable border plants for a lawn are carpet bugle *(Ajuga reptans)*, the creeping-stemmed European violet *(Viola odorata)*, and green, purple and variegated forms of a dwarf wintercreeper *(Euonymus)*.

The planting of ground covers is also a way of extending the lawn into an area that is too moist and shady for grass. European wild ginger *(Asarum europaeum)* and galax *(Galax aphylla)* are two splendid plants for this purpose. Another is the plant known variously as moneywort, creeping Jenny and creeping Charlie *(Lysimachia nummularia)*. It hugs the ground about as closely as any creeping ground cover, and sends out long delicate-looking shoots of very light green shiny leaves.

Yellow flowers appear all along the stems in spring. It is thoroughly hardy and can become invasive if it is too much at home.

## Ground Covers and Paving Stones

Ground covers may be combined very successfully with paving stones in an outdoor living area. The stones must, of course, be laid dry, that is, without cement. Irregular shapes are best. Place the stones quite far apart, working them into the ground a little so that the top of the stones and the top of the plants will be fairly level. Then put mat-like plants in the spaces between the stones.

For an all-green planting, moss sandwort *(Arenaria verna caespitosa)* is excellent. It hugs the ground closely, looks very like moss, bears tiny white star-like flowers, spreads rapidly, stands tramping, tolerates both sun and shade, and is thoroughly hardy.

A paving stone planting is also a way of using rock garden plants without making a rock garden. Apart from the fact that many of the plants best suited for this purpose like sun, this is a kind of planting that is prettiest in a bright light. Varieties of creeping thyme *(Thymus)*, with white and rose-colored flowers, and leaves that are green and shiny or gray and woolly, make a charming pattern and release fragrance when the plants are bruised. Rock garden pinks *(Dianthus)* are another useful group. Especially good varieties are the maiden pink *(Dianthus deltoides)*, the sand pink *(Dianthus arenarius)*, and the cheddar pink *(Dianthus caesius)*. Anyone who becomes really interested in this type of planting will want to pursue the subject in specialty books about alpines and other rock garden plants. The selection of plants, of course, depends on the amount of traffic in the area.

## Many-Purpose Ground Covers

The three most valuable and widely used plants for providing a rich evergreen ground cover upholstery are English ivy *(Hedera helix)*, myrtle or periwinkle *(Vinca minor)* and Japanese spurge *(Pachysandra terminalis)*.

English ivy will grow in almost any soil and under almost

any condition. An ivy planting is practically everlasting and increasingly handsome. An old bed becomes virtually self-sustaining, with humus created by decaying leaves and moisture retained under a thick mat. Baltic ivy (*Hedera helix baltica*) is hardier and less luxuriant. In mild climates, the tender Asiatic ivies, with larger leaves and more lush growth, can be grown. They are usually sold as Javanese or California ivy.

Though ivy will gradually take hold in very poor soil, to get it started quickly, plant in rich soil and don't neglect watering. In city gardens especially, ivy plantings are vastly improved if they are given a frequent good hosing.

*Vinca minor* does well in shade once it is established, but it may be slower starting there than in sun. One of its great charms is the small lavender flowers in early spring.

Though in time it may become a heavy mat, myrtle is a finer-textured plant than ivy and often prettiest when it is not too luxuriant. When a planting of English ivy becomes thick, there is always a sense of pattern because the young growth, which often has an upward thrust, is light against the darker background of the old leaves, but with myrtle there is not this contrast and a very thick planting may look merely healthy. Too much may even be a little funereal. All in all, though, myrtle is one of the very best ground covers. It may not be evergreen in its northern limits of hardiness.

Pachysandra is valuable in the most highly manicured gardens as well as in very simple informal gardens. It has a wide range of hardiness. In freezing weather, the leaves darken and droop, but they revive as soon as the temperature rises, and any burning they may suffer is usually not apparent until the new growth has already started.

Pachysandra is excellent in the heavy shade of trees such as the Norway maple. In a small city garden, it is pretty in little informal clumps, to provide evergreen touches in winter. A border of pachysandra sets off a paved area. It may be used to outline a shrub planting. It is less satisfactory in full sun than in shade and in this respect it is inferior to ivy and myrtle.

Rooted cuttings should be set about six inches apart. Pachysandra does not require a lot of water, but it will suffer badly and perhaps not recover if it is allowed to get thoroughly dry.

## Ground Covers for Large Areas

For relatively large areas (which may exist even in a "small" garden, especially if the ground slopes steeply, or if the house is perched on a bank above the street), strong-growing plants are best; but the texture of the surface to be covered should not be overlooked. For instance, if the ground is studded with handsome stones, the planting should not conceal the stones but make a pattern with them.

Grape vines and Virginia creeper (*Parthenocissus quinque-folia*) both make excellent inexpensive deciduous coverings for a large area in a very short time. Virginia creeper provides brilliant fall color; the leaves of most grapes have a bold and satisfying texture. In the wild riverbank or frost grape, hardy into northern Canada, the flowers are sweetly scented. The young shoots of a Manchurian species (*Vitis amurensis*) are reddish and the handsome foliage turns crimson and purple in fall. The slender-stemmed *Vitis thunbergi* of Japan becomes a rich red in autumn. The two last-named may be hard to get.

Two roses excellent for draping banks or a steep approach to a house are the memorial rose (*Rosa wichuraiana*), with small white flowers, and the more dramatic Max Graf, with large single pink flowers. Max Graf has the distinctive, rather rough foliage typical of the rugosa breed. Flanking steps cut into a steep ascent, either of these roses is handsome. Roses leaf out early in spring, and the thorny stems of a strong-growing rose have their own particular beauty in winter.

Prostrate forms of juniper will cover a bank with a shaggy mat of gray-green, blue-green tinged with purple, or just green, depending on the variety. The Bar Harbor juniper, with gray-green foliage, is especially lovely. This variety, also the shore juniper (*Juniperus conferta*) and the Sargent juniper (*Juniperus chinensis sargenti*) are all splendid for shore plantings. Junipers need sun. They usually look better in the vicinity of rough gray stone than any other type of masonry, and may look very out of place near harsh new brick.

The creeping and semi-prostrate cotoneasters, with flat sprays of tiny leaves and handsome red berries, are good for a rocky bank. The foliage does not make a dense curtain and the tendency of the plants to arch a little prevents them from smothering the stones. One of the best known is the rock spray cotoneaster *(Cotoneaster horizontalis)*, but there are several low growing species, with small variations in size of leaves and manner of growth.

The heaths and heathers are beautiful ground covers, but not right for every situation and more difficult to use than the other plants mentioned. In a finer way, the texture is comparable to that of juniper—rather rough and billowing. Soil that is acid and poor in quality, some moisture, and sun are needed. Heather *(Calluna)* is somewhat hardier than heath *(Erica)*. Unless these plants can be grown well it is better to avoid them altogether.

For a difficult city situation, or a quick temporary cover, don't forget the sweet potato and the yam. Anyone who has seen sweet potatoes clambering among lovely old ancestor jars in the terraced gardens of South China will recognize their decorative possibilities. With the increase of Spanish grocery shops to meet the needs of new arrivals in this country, plant introduction is being unofficially extended. Some of the tender, vine-producing tubers are worth investigating.

## Ground Covers for Special Purposes

Some ground covers are especially effective as an underplanting for a particular tree or shrub. Their use, however, calls for discrimination and it is a good idea to visualize different kinds in combination with various shrubs and trees. Epimedium, for instance, is delightful under a red-leafed Japanese maple; the light green of the leaves on little wiry stems is a good complement to the airy Japanese maple and less somber than ivy or myrtle. In Plates 25 and 26, following page 192, sword ferns make a strong-textured base for the rugged trunk of an old apple tree.

## Miscellaneous Ground Covers

There are scores of ground covers. Many plants listed as ground covers are quite tall and suitable for only very large-scale landscaping; it is wise, therefore, to check the height when buying. Following is a short list of useful, well known ground cover plants not mentioned above:

SUN

*Arabis alpina* (Alpine Rock Cress)
*Arctostaphylos uva-ursi* (Bearberry)
*Cornus canadensis* (Bunchberry)
*Duchesnea indica* (Mock Strawberry)
*Fragaria* (Strawberry)
*Liriope spicata* (Creeping Lily-turf)
*Nepeta hederacea* (Ground-ivy)
*Phlox subulata* (Moss-pink)
*Sedum* in variety

SHADE

*Armeria maritima* (Thrift)
*Asperula odorata* (Sweet Woodruff)
*Convallaria majalis* (Lily of the Valley)
*Lonicera japonica halliana* (Hall's Honeysuckle)—Use cautiously, it is highly invasive.
*Myosotis scorpioides* (Forget-me-not)
*Nepeta hederacea* (Ground-ivy)
*Ophiopogon japonicum* (Dwarf Lily-turf)
*Vaccinium angustifolium laevifolium* (Lowbush Blueberry)

## Chapter VII

# *FLOWERS*

Not their beauty alone should account for the pleasure with which the gardener sets out to choose the flowers that will brighten his yard from spring to frost, or, in some parts of the country, the year round. For, in the ideal garden, the making of flower beds means that the garden has been laid out, and the big chores done. Relax you may, with the comfortable thought that whatever you do won't upset the major scheme. To remake a walk or move a tree is an onerous task, but if you are dissatisfied with the results of a flower planting, changes are easy. Indeed, many people like a different flower dress every year, or at least some fresh embellishments.

"Flowers" are generally assumed to mean perennials, annuals, bulbs, and roses. This is, of course, a loose way of talking, because shrubs and trees produce flowers, too, but it is a generally accepted way and everyone knows what is meant. In garden literature, the flower planting is often called the herbaceous planting, or the herbaceous border. Actually, it may include plants that are not grown for their flowers at all, but for their bright showy leaves. This is especially true in the far South, where foliage plants such as crotons are used a good deal to supply color. Even in the North, such plants as coleus, red-leafed begonias, and plants in which the green of the leaves is splashed with white, are grown in borders either entirely for their foliage, or as much for their foliage as for their flowers.

As one moves North, the distinction between perennial and annual plants, or, in other words, those that endure from year to year and those that must be planted afresh each season, becomes sharper, until, in the coldest areas, a rigid planting routine is established. No one who has lived only in a warm climate can fully appreciate the frenzy of a northern garden calendar, and the careful thought that goes into insuring a procession of color, from the first crocus, when the snow is still on the ground, to the last chrysanthemum, when frost has laid low the less stalwart soldiers of the border. Southern gardeners sometimes feel that they are unjustly charged with a certain languor about gardening; what is perhaps not always realized is that northern gardeners must press their program into a half-year. Dates acquire a significance they cannot have in a mild climate.

## Fashions in Flowers

There is probably no phase of gardening in which fashions have changed more than in the use of flowers. It is difficult to pinpoint all the reasons, but a few may be mentioned. One is the trend in domestic architecture. The modern builder seeks novelty and diversity, creating structural designs that make old standard flower patterns in the surrounding area absurd. The picture window has been introduced, changing the indoors view of the garden from a niggardly glimpse to a full-scale canvas. Many more types of building material are available, making the texture of backgrounds against which plants are seen more varied. Brick planters for low-growing things are not infrequently built out from the foundations; these are especially popular in the South and invite a frieze or ribbon of color near the base of the house. The inside living-room often merges into the outdoor living area, which in turn merges into the garden, giving enormous scope for patio type planting.

All these developments are symptoms of a freer, more imaginative approach to living, and, naturally, the mood is reflected in the choice and use of plants. Garden ideas from other countries, especially countries in the Orient, instead of being slavishly imitated are made the springboard for ingenious adaptations. This is a most refreshing departure.

THE PERENNIAL BORDER. Other reasons are social and economic. For instance, the increased cost of labor has contributed to the decline in popularity of the perennial border. A well-made perennial border, with a backbone of such strong-growing favorites as phlox and delphiniums and asters and peonies is a magnificent sight, but such a border requires careful preparation and continuing care. Since most perennials bloom only for a limited period, a badly planned or ill-kept border presents recurring gaps. Many annuals, on the other hand, do not let up from spring to frost. Home owners pressed for time and money find it simpler, therefore, to depend on a few kinds of annuals for a summer-long display. The supply always reflects the demand, and the decreased demand for perennials has been an enormous impetus to the development of new varieties of annuals. The list swells every year, and the difference between varieties in a big group such as marigolds can be so great as to produce totally different effects.

FLOWER ARRANGEMENT.    Another significant influence on flower fashions is the wide interest in flower arrangement. The criterion for many women gardeners is the usefulness of a plant's foliage, flowers or seed pods in an arrangement.

Any discussion of flowers has thus become much more complex than it was when Peter Henderson wrote *Gardening for Pleasure* in 1905. His ideal was the Victorian ideal of a geometrical bed tightly packed with plants in graded heights, so arranged that a pattern of color was rigidly presented. This type of planting still lingers in public gardens, around war memorials and flagpoles, and in the round poultices that dot the lawns of some suburban and semi-rural areas. Red salvia figures prominently in these little beds, combined with geraniums, begonias and coleus. Such beds are literally period pieces just as much as an antimacassar or a Victorian ornament with dangling bits of cut glass. And, when well done and in the proper place, they do not invariably deserve a sophisticated shudder. They may, in fact, sometimes be just right and a lot of fun to make.

## Culture

Because of their rather distinctive uses and, to some extent, their special needs, roses and bulbs are treated in separate chapters. Generally speaking, the other plants for the flower bed—perennials and annuals grown for their bloom and herbaceous plants grown for their foliage—tolerate a wide range of soil types of average fertility. While some kinds will not grow in shade, and others do not thrive in sun, for many the shade-sun line is finely drawn. Quite often a plant that is listed as sun-loving does very nicely in fairly shady locations. These observations should not be taken to mean, however, that flower beds flourish with any old treatment. Watering should be adequate and the top inch of soil should be kept loose. Weeds steal nutriment and impoverish the planting. For perennials, the soil should be well prepared and fertile to a depth of eighteen inches. Drainage must be good.

## Flowers as Part of the Design

Though flowers per se come last in the making of a garden, they are still an integral part of the design. In a sense they are trimming; but they are much more than trimming. Just as a splash of dramatic color can be an arresting and memorable feature of a painting, so can a clump of flowers of the right color in the right place bring a garden to life. What the beginner so often fails to realize is that the background design does as much for the flowers as the flowers do for the design. This is why it is important, when you are attracted to a growing plant, to notice its surroundings. This may contribute just as much to the impression it makes on you as the plant itself, and if you rush to buy one like it and put it in a totally different situation you may be disappointed.

When the garden was planned, the location of flower beds or flower clumps was decided. Some gardeners will have these areas visualized, at the planning stage, right down to the last plant; others are content merely to determine their position, with more or less precision, according to the type of treatment they are to receive. For instance, flower pockets in front of shrubs must remain more or less fluid on the plan, whereas dimensioned beds should be strictly defined.

The type of plants to use depends a great deal on the location, not only from the standpoint of sun and shade but visually. Obviously, for example, if the flowers are to be viewed from a distance, coarse textures and strong colors are more effective than delicate plants and pale flowers. In choosing plants to put near windows and patios, fragrance may be even more important than appearance, especially if the areas close to the flowers are used more in the evening than in daylight. When the area is a transition area from indoors to outdoors, the color of furniture and curtains may influence the choice of plants. In this way flowers can be used to complement interior decoration.

To some extent, the type of flower planting that is most successful in any one garden changes from year to year, as trees and shrubs grow and take on individual qualities. Every gardener who has lived with his trees and shrubs for years is familiar with the emergence of a subtle pattern that distinguishes his planting from that of his neighbors: a branch is broken and the shape of a tree is changed; a prevailing wind produces a slight stoop; an undetermined quality in the soil results in unforeseen vigor, or the reverse. The big woody things in the garden are the background of the flowers, and if the background changes the flower pattern may need revising, too.

Even without these changes, the gardener rarely sees all the possibilities of effective detail at once. He may feel a vague dissatisfaction about some corner of the garden, and then in a flash realize just what is needed to put it right. All this helps to make a garden fun, and to keep it a living creative interest rather than something that has merely to be maintained.

## Kinds of Flowers

Now let us discuss in a little more detail the plants available for this finishing of the design. Next to culinary and medicinal herbs, herbaceous flowering plants have attracted more local and folk names than other classes of plants. To mention this is not irrelevant, because it introduces subtle literary and emotional overtones that undoubtedly influence the feeling of many people about a plant. Bleeding heart, cherry pie, Dutchman's breeches, monkshood, columbine, coral bells, London pride, snow-in-summer, love-in-a-mist, snapdragons, Jacob's ladder: these are common names for familiar and beloved perennials and annuals. Oddly enough, some of the finest and most popular herbaceous plants have not been given common names: *Delphinium, Gaillardia* and *Chrysanthemum* (unless one accepts the horrible abbreviation of "mum") are three examples. Others, though they have common names, are usually referred to by their Latin name. This gives a curious verbal imbalance to conversation about flowers, which I have often observed is bewildering to a beginner.

## Perennials

Perennials vary in size from small mat- or mound-like plants, useful between stepping stones or as edgings for a flower bed, to plants several feet high that occupy the space of a shrub. In winter they die to the ground; in spring, year after year, new growth springs from the roots, some varieties to flower in spring, others in summer, and still others not till fall. Perennials include big groups of popular garden plants, such as chrysanthemums, daylilies, iris and peonies. The variation within these giant groups is so great that each is a subject in itself. There are, in addition, many other perennials that have not attracted the attention of hybridizers and remain groups of a very few species and perhaps one or two horticultural forms. These are usually very dependable plants under a wide range of conditions. Examples are perennial alyssum, rock cress, bleeding heart, monkshood, artemisia, bugbane, coreopsis, leopard's-bane, globe thistle, gaillardia, galax, gypsophila, sneezeweed, coral bells, lavender, forget-me-not. There are many more.

A PROCESSION OF BLOOM. When a collection of perennials is grown together in one bed, they must be selected so that there is always some bloom distributed in a pleasing pattern throughout the border. Jarring colors must be avoided in varieties that flower at the same time. A method that avoids this complicated planning and is often most satisfactory in a small garden, is to plant clumps of perennials in front of shrubs or near a wall or a rock. This kind of planting gives a procession of bloom throughout the whole garden, a sort of seasonal motion picture focussing attention first on one part and then on another. There is something very pleasing about the annual reappearance of an old floral friend, and, by thoughtful placing, this use of perennials can supplement the flowers of shrubs. For instance, early blooming flowers such as bleeding heart, iris, peonies and oriental poppies may be planted near shrubs whose flowers or fruits are not conspicuous until late in the season.

CHRYSANTHEMUMS. The unique value of chrysanthemums is the life they bring to the garden at a time when other flowers are fading or have already folded their petals. Their marvelous fall palette in shades of yellow, bronze and red may be used against the background of a spring-flowering shrub that has long since become an indeterminate mass of green. Or they may be used to complement the picture of a vividly colored tree or shrub. The sparkling white varieties can be used to enormous effect. Chrysanthemums stand rough handling and can be dug up just before flowering to replace zinnias or other annuals that are becoming shabby in a border.

The variation in flower form of chrysanthemums, from simple daisy-like blooms to voluptuous heads of reflexed petals, makes them equally useful for casual plantings in a cottage garden and for dramatic accents in a sophisticated planting. The large-flowered kinds can be extremely handsome in ornamental containers in a patio.

Within any one type, the difference between hundreds of chrysanthemums is often negligible except to a specialist. The grower is advised to learn the difference between the important types and then choose by color.

DAYLILIES. Daylilies *(Hemerocallis)* are another important group of perennials with a wide range of ornamental value. They have become a darling of the hybridizers and have evolved mightily from the lemon lily of old New England gardens. It is now possible to get varieties for early, mid-season and late flowering, so that they can be used for a summer-long planting pattern in a way that most perennials cannot. Colors are every shade of yellow, buff, copper and pink. The exotic quality of the blooms belies the toughness and hardiness of the plants. They make splendid accent plants. They are also excellent as a massed planting, or scattered informally near trees in a semi-wild area.

THE SMALLER PERENNIALS. Among the smaller perennials, rock cress *(Arabis alpina)* makes a charming edging for a bed of tulips. The lacy white flowers in early spring combine beautifully with the bulbs. Coral bells *(Heuchera)* is another good edging plant; the basal rosette of pinkish leaves is pretty with or without the slender spikes of pink, white or red flowers. The fringed bleeding heart *(Dicentra eximia)* makes a soft mound of gray green foliage all season and the pink or white flowers are produced for many weeks. The old-time favorite, *Dicentra spectabilis,* a larger and more lovely plant, is declining in popularity because of its short blooming period. Also, the leaves disappear almost immediately after flowering, and it is easy to injure the fleshy roots when digging. If a spot can be found in the garden where it will not be disturbed it will do a great deal for the early spring picture. A low gray stone wall sets off to perfection its delicate sprays of pink heart-shaped flowers.

PERENNIALS WITH ORNAMENTAL FOLIAGE. The foliage of perennials ranges through every shade of green, gray-green and blue-green, and in texture may be smooth or woolly, finely cut, or have large simple planes. This diversity is important in the over-all pattern of a mixed planting, but generally speaking the leaves of perennials are not outstanding for their decorative value. The following plants are notable exceptions:

*Hosta*, known also as plantain lily and funkia. The flowers, which may be white, blue, or lavender, are borne on slender stalks, in most varieties high above the heavy basal rosette of leaves. Hostas are valuable ornamentals in shady places and under trees, but it is for the usefulness of their lustrous foliage in flower arrangement that they are probably most esteemed today. *H. alba marginata* has large leaves edged with a broad band of white. In *H. fortunei viridis marginata* the large pointed leaves are olive green with a margin of darker green. The leaves of *H. fortunei gigantea* and *H. glauca* are blue-green and crinkled. A narrow-leafed variety is *H. lancifolia albo-marginata.*

*Bergenia cordifolia*, sometimes called saxifrage. The delicate flowers are pink or purplish-pink on a long stalk; the rounded leaves are glossy, leathery, and extraordinarily handsome. It is a beautiful plant to grow by itself among rocks.

*Sedum spectabile*, called the live-for-ever plant because of its almost indestructible quality. The flowers are pink in late summer; the leaves are gray-green or red-green and very fleshy. In late fall, clumps of live-for-ever plant, with dried flower heads and yellowing foliage, retain their form and substance and are quite decorative.

*Ruta graveolens* is the rue of herb collections, but it deserves a place in any garden for its highly individual, blue-green foliage. Though the leaves look lacy, they are amazingly tough and retain their freshness well after the early frosts.

To sum up, every texture and shade of foliage are to be found among perennials, every color in the flowers, and an enormous range in the size and type of growth. It is impossible in a book of this scope to do more than throw out a few hints of their beauty and usefulness.

## Annuals

Annuals are excellent plants with which to try out color effects in a new garden. They are also useful for temporary planting in places where permanent work must be postponed. Their transience permits a gardener to be reckless and venturesome. They are good practice plants for the inexperienced. And for those whose gardening energy declines after a burst of spring enthusiasm they are heaven-sent; many varieties will provide good-looking beds from Easter to the end of the season.

The new seed catalogs are mailed early in the new year; this is the time to make lists and prepare orders. Lists are much easier to compile if garden centers and botanical gardens have been visited the previous summer and notes made on named varieties. For a number of years, each season has produced such a spate of fresh varieties that the descriptions of popular groups such as petunias, marigolds and zinnias may run into several pages. To have seen and evaluated a few varieties in bloom is an enormous help. These can be used for places where you want to be sure of what you are buying, leaving others for less critical locations. No illustrated description, be it never so accurate, can convey a picture to a reader that compares with the actual plant.

Many catalogs give useful hints about the time to sow seed, whether the location should be sunny or shady, and whether germination and growth will be so slow that it is wise, in areas where spring is late, to start the seed indoors. Some people love to putter with flats and containers in a heated porch or on a window sill; others prefer to wait until the maples are in leaf and it is warm enough to sow outdoors in an open bed. For the window sill growers, small flats of plastic and aluminum foil, and one- to five-pound bags of prepared soil are available at garden supply stores. Most annuals are very easy to grow by following the simple directions on the seed packet. An occasional failure only adds to one's experience.

For those who do not want to bother with seed, young plants of varying size that have been forced in greenhouses are plentiful around Easter. Seedling plants get the garden off to an early start and can be supplemented by seed of the same varieties scattered among the plants. The seed produces a second crop to take the place of early plants that get shabby.

A FEW KINDS ARE ENOUGH. Using only varieties of what are probably the three most popular annuals—marigolds, petunias and zinnias—it is possible to obtain as many kinds of flowers as you are likely to need. Let us take these three groups in turn.

MARIGOLDS. With some plants, the intensity of the light in which they are to be viewed is an important part of their effectiveness. Marigolds, though they will tolerate some shade, are usually most exciting in bright sunlight. This is especially true of the orange and mahogany-red varieties. Marigolds seem to be especially good when nearby structural material is a dark-colored wood, and where rocks and earth have a raw, reddish-brown look. This may seem a rather wild generalization, but marigolds are hot plants visually and some of this quality is lost in pallid surroundings.

Though marigolds are splendid for providing splashes of brilliant color in a mixed planting, they do not combine especially well with other plants. This is not to say that they are a jarring note, but one does not instinctively pair them with another flower as a natural companion.

In size, marigolds range from rank, shrub-like plants over three feet high to dwarf varieties and species bearing tiny blooms only a few inches from the ground. The foliage in the husky kinds is often coarse; it should be observed when evaluating a variety. All marigolds are so striking that they are excellent distance plants, either in clumps or as a sheet of solid color. The Petite class of very dwarf, bedding-type marigolds are splendid for small, tight plantings, and for edging accents in a large bed. The dwarf singles, such as Naughty Marietta, are for a more spreading, relaxed effect. An especially beautiful variety in this class is Red Head, with rich, wallflower-colored flowers. Among the giant sorts, with three- to four-inch flowers, sometimes ruffled, the pale, creamy-yellow varieties soften the harsh oranges when they are grown side by side. A defect to avoid is the greenish tinge of some yellow varieties; this has been a flaw in specimens of Yellow Climax that I have seen.

PETUNIAS.   Petunias, unlike marigolds, are wonderful blending plants. They combine beautifully with such plants as verbena, annual phlox, snapdragons, sweet alyssum, ageratum, and, indeed, any number of pastel-toned flowers and flowers in which the bright colors are pink or blue or purple. White petunias are a leavener in any planting.

A bed containing heliotrope and white and violet-purple petunias is both lovely and fragrant, and especially satisfactory near a patio. There are bright red and bright salmon petunias, but they are less attractive in my opinion than the pinks and purples and rich shades of blue-violet and burgundy. One of the most truly hideous flower plantings I have seen was a bed of red petunias in front of a long stretch of crude red brick wall.

Petunias are more subtle flowers than marigolds, and the situations in which they are effective are rarely interchangeable with those in which marigolds are the perfect answer. The loose, floppy kinds, as contrasted with the more compact bedding types, are very useful along the edges of plantings that are raised a foot or more above the general level of the garden or patio.

ZINNIAS.   For many people, zinnias are *the* outstanding annual. Painters love them. It is fortunate that most people are familiar with zinnias, because any attempt to describe them makes one realize how inadequate words are to express the essential quality of a flower. As plants, zinnias are not beautiful. Growth is awkward; the foliage is nondescript and tends to get mildewy towards the end of the season; yet the over-all effect of a bed of zinnias, or even of a few zinnias in a mixed bed, is full of character.

The color range is greater than in either marigolds or petunias. Some people dislike the magenta shades, which may be fairly numerous in a packet of mixed seed, but for me its omission in a zinnia planting is a woeful defect. For the magenta haters, and those who want only specific colors, named varieties are available. Among these Isabellina is a most lovely creamy buttercup yellow, Pink Lady a patrician pink shading to buff, and Oriole a magnificent orange-gold.

There are several types of zinnias, besides the giant plain, dahlia-flowered and cactus-flowered kinds, and though the low-growing pompon varieties usually turn out to be taller than one had hoped, the flowers are small. The 1963 catalogs list a new dwarf zinnia, Thumbelina, which, if it lives up to the claims made for it will be valuable in small gardens. Aesthetically, zinnias are a curious mixture of boldness and subtlety; it is hard to think of a situation in which they are out of place. Their worst, perhaps their only, defect is that they get shabby towards the end of summer. It is therefore wise to grow them where they can be removed late in the season without leaving an offensive gap, or where they can be replaced by chrysanthemums.

OTHER ANNUALS. There are hundreds of other annuals, with greater and lesser degrees of usefulness. Many possess great beauty and most have devoted admirers and lend themselves especially to some specific use. Here are a few:

For rather coarse but brilliant effects in colors that range through amethyst, silver-green, pink, orange and scarlet, there is celosia, with cockscomb and plume-headed types. The former lends itself to a dramatic type of flower arrangement; the latter to massing in a distant part of the garden.

Snapdragons, petunias, heliotrope, nicotiana and sweet alyssum are fragrant annuals. Impatiens, white and in shades of salmon and pink, flowers from spring to frost in quite heavy shade. Colored varieties of alyssum provide carpets of pink or purple or violet all summer. Larkspur, anchusa, and the lace flower (*Didiscus*) bring soft and vivid tones of blue to the garden. Portulaca is for brilliant splashes in rocky areas in full sun. The pastel shades and powder-puff texture of ageratum are lovely in a soft light. Rose, bronze and red snapdragons make good minor accents in a planting; the whites and soft yellows are cooling.

And so on. Annuals are described and illustrated in hundreds of catalogs, and grown in trial plots that are open to the public all over the land. In one short season an annual tells its whole story; there is no need to wait and wonder and be patient. While the rest of the garden is slowly unfolding, often maddeningly bashful about revealing its full charms, the annuals come and go, able to present as many dresses in as many years as the whim of the gardener demands.

## Roses

*(Written in collaboration with Roberta Lord, Landscape Architect.)*

"A rose is a rose is a rose" wrote Gertrude Stein with unassailable truth. For a gardener, a rose may also be a covering for a wall, a rock garden plant, a hedge plant, a shrub, a screen, or a splash of all-season color. Indeed, the enormously creative work of rose hybridizers in the last few decades has so enlarged the usefulness of the rose that it has replaced perennials in many gardens.

THREE BROAD CLASSES. For the small garden, three broad classes of roses are especially useful: climbing roses, various shrubby types, and the repeat-blooming bush roses. A characteristic of all these is the large amount of bloom they supply for the space they occupy. The largest climbers need only a square foot or so of ground and their blooms may be legion. The bush kinds take, at most, a two- to three-foot spacing, and bloom from spring to frost. There are shrubby kinds most happily in scale for small areas, some that bloom all season, and others that bloom only once a year, but abundantly.

A climbing rose can be supported by a single pillar or post, spread flat on a trellis against a garage or house wall, allowed to scramble over a boundary fence or wall, trained over an architectural feature such as an archway or pergola, or used to screen a patio or porch. There are even climbing roses that can be used as ground covers and are particularly useful for covering a steep, sunny bank.

The repeat-blooming bush types of roses are useful, above all, as long-lived plants to bloom over a very long season in the same spot in the garden. In a rose planting, there is always something new to see, morning, noon or evening, day after day, from spring to frost. Almost as soon as a bloom is cut, new growth starts again from the stem; it may be bright lettuce-green or mahogany colored, or anywhere between, depending on variety. Opening buds are different every hour of the day.

The range of color and form of these types of roses, and their size and fragrance, give almost unlimited choice in creating garden pictures to suit an individual taste, or the site.

LOCATION AND SOIL. To give continuous bloom in quantity, roses need sunlight for at least about half a day; if there is a choice, morning sunlight has some advantages in drying dew from the foliage as promptly as possible. They also need good air circulation. If their place is a very airy one, the time of day of their sunlight exposure will matter less. They can take, gratefully, full sunlight and an amazing amount of breeziness.

They need a fertile soil, deeply dug, with large amounts of humus, thoroughly mixed to the full depth of digging. This can be peat moss, well decayed manure, leaves, compost, or any combination of these. A series of tests conducted at Cornell University showed that the more humus the better, even up to a mixture of half and half soil and peat moss.

Though all varieties appear to do best in a soil that is just slightly acid, some have a wider tolerance than others and this often explains why certain varieties do better in one area then another. This slightly acid condition is easy enough to obtain and maintain in the small space required by each rose plant, so testing and changing the acidity or alkalinity of the soil is usually more satisfactory than trying to find varieties that will tolerate special conditions. Peat moss will do much to correct some over-alkalinity; a little powdered sulphur will give good results in more strongly alkaline soils, which can then be kept right by using slightly acid fertilizer mixtures or cottonseed meal. Lime, of course, will correct any amount of over-acidity.

AMPLE WATER AND GOOD DRAINAGE. Roses also require a combination of ample water and good drainage. They cannot tolerate stagnant water about their roots but seem to endure almost any amount of water moving freely through the soil. Their minimum need for full bloom all summer is an inch of water a week and they thrive under irrigation or hose soaking whenever rainfall is inadequate. In order to control fungus diseases on the foliage, it is better to let the water run directly on the soil than to sprinkle the whole plant.

SEASONAL CARE. Research chemists and inventors have taken

the labor out of the seasonal care of rose plants. Present-day all-purpose sprays are enormously efficient and do not discolor the flowers or leave unpleasant odors in their wake. There are many types of sprayers that are quick and easy to use; the kind in which water in a hose does the work of diluting and pumping the spray material has reduced this chore to a matter of moments, even for a large planting. There are also a herbicide that prevents weed seeds from sprouting in the rose bed, and mulches that make soil cultivation unnecessary throughout the summer.

Roses seem to like being worked with and even fussed over, and this quality has an undoubted appeal for many persons.

ROSE CLASSES.   The reader will have gathered that roses exist in almost bewildering variety; but an understanding of how the different classes are ordinarily grouped makes the picture much clearer. It should be understood that "classes" are very largely "groupings of convenience" that are in general use and have evolved from the facts of the roses themselves. Some few varieties may be classed differently in different places, and new classes may well be added in the future, whenever a group of roses is developed that just will not fit any present classification.

Any attempt to group roses by color, within any class, runs into difficulties. Most roses change in shade or tint as they develop from bud to full bloom. Their coloring varies with soil and climate. Many have the sort of subtle overtones found in certain types of silk and brocade. A rose may be different if grown in full sun or partial shade; practically all colored roses have a deeper, richer color in the cool days of fall than they do in midsummer heat. There is the added problem that different people see colors differently and color names mean different things to different people. Where does light red leave off and deep pink begin, for example? Bearing in mind all this fluidity in roses, we can proceed to the groupings, which, after all, are helpful and reasonably workable, despite the difficulties.

REPEAT-BLOOMING BUSH ROSES.   The most widely grown roses today are the three groups of repeat-blooming bush roses: hybrid teas, floribundas and grandifloras. These three groups also account for the largest number of varieties that are widely available, though a great many varieties of other types can be found. (Climbing roses, especially, are easy to get in great variety; these are considered separately, later.) In fact, the number of varieties available in any rose class is so great, and so subject to constant change, as new varieties are developed and older ones dropped from commerce, that it is not possible in the scope of this book to mention more than a few representative kinds in each class. Those mentioned are all well known varieties whose virtues and habits have been widely tested and proved.

HYBRID TEAS. These usually produce their flowers one to a stem, with the blooms held upright. Buds and bloom are good sized, of the form seen everywhere on greeting cards and damask tablecloths; they are the kind you ordinarily get when ordering cut roses from the florist. They may have five petals or more than a hundred or anywhere between. They are mostly fragrant, especially when newly opening and in the morning before the sun volatilizes their perfume oil. By and large, their perfume is likely to be heavier and more persistent in the deeper colors than in the very light to white ones. There are many varieties in countless shades, tints and combinations of crimson, red, pink, yellow and white and a few newer kinds that shade towards lavender, or brown, from sun-tan to coffee. Up to the moment of writing, there is no true blue, though the lavender ones contain blue, as do some of the red and pink ones, so bluer roses are probably not impossible. In the early years of this century, yellow hybrid teas were as rare and new, and caused as much furor pro and con, as lavender and tan ones in the 1960's.

Hybrid teas produce sturdy plants with good foliage, and can be grown over an extremely wide area of the United States, as well as elsewhere throughout the world. For most of the country they need nothing more than a mound of earth over the base of each plant or no protection at all, during their dormant season. They should not be fertilized or watered during late summer and fall in areas where frost or freezing weather is likely to follow.

## Representative Varieties of Hybrid Teas

*Crimson Red:* Crimson Glory; Chrysler Imperial; Christopher Stone; Etoile de Hollande; Nocturne; Mirandy. (Crimson

Glory tends to a low, spreading growth; it is a "front row" type of plant. Mirandy has extra-large flowers with considerable blue in the crimson, especially in the full blooms and under certain growing conditions.)

*Other Shades of Red:* Grande Duchesse Charlotte, medium red with more than a hint of chestnut-red in its coloring; Tallyho, different but somewhat in the same direction; New Yorker, bright, deep red; Texas Centennial, somewhere between brick red and deep pink; Charlotte Armstrong, deep pink or light red. (These are all strong growers, tending to taller growth than any of the crimson varieties above.)

*Pink—from deep to light in order:* Charlotte Armstrong (as above); Show Girl; Pink Peace; Dr. Debat; The Doctor; Radiance; First Love; Confidence.

*Salmon-pink to Peach:* Helen Traubel; Mme. Cochet-Cochet; Good News; Duquesa de Penaranda.

*Other Pinks:* Mme. Henri Guillot, brilliant, deep blend of many shades; President Herbert Hoover, pink, salmon and yellow blend; Symphony, deep pink and silver blend; Mojave, deep coppery pink blend.

*Pure Yellow:* Lowell Thomas; Mrs. P. S. duPont (low-growing, spreading, very floriferous, another front-row kind); Eclipse, very long pointed buds; Soeur Therese (the tallest growing of this group, but none of them can be classed as tall).

*Other Yellows:* Peace, yellow with a varying edging of pink on the petals, very large blooms, stems and plants; Sutter's Gold, yellow, red-gold and copper blend.

*White:* White Knight; Blanche Mallerin; Mme. Jules Bouche.

*Other Whites:* Garden Party. This is not a white rose at all, when seen close up, but its delicate ivory and pink tints show up as a gleaming white from a short distance, so for landscape use it is an extremely valuable rose for giving a white effect. Its plant gives a better mass than do any of the really white hybrid teas, for places where this is needed.

## Single Hybrid Teas

(Five petals to each flower): Dainty Bess, the classic pink single. Golden Wings is sometimes listed with hybrid teas, but, for garden use, it belongs with the everblooming shrub roses because of its manner of growth. There are other single hybrid teas with beautiful flower color, but, to date, none that is widely satisfactory in plant growth.

FLORIBUNDAS.  Floribundas produce fair-sized blooms in large clusters. They are very floriferous and some are extremely hardy. They make plants of good mass, usually between two and three feet tall and often broader than high, though some will grow taller if pruning is restrained. Floribunda color range is similar to that of hybrid teas, with many extremely brilliant colors that carry for a great distance. They are a newer type than hybrid teas and though there are attractive yellow varieties the outstanding yellow floribunda is yet to come. There is a wide range of form in individual blooms but fragrance in this class is slight.

*Varieties*

*Red:* Red Pinocchio; Frensham; Alain; World's Fair; Garnette; Red Wonder; Red Favorite. (All very good and there are many other good reds.)

*Orange-red:* Coccorico and Sarabande, both brilliant; Floradora, a softer, subtle shade. (Others with great promise are fast appearing in this color range.)

*Pink:* Betty Prior, deep pink and will grow very tall if permitted; Else Poulsen, medium pink, very hardy, medium tall; Cecile Brunner (the Sweetheart Rose), small plant and flowers; Pinocchio. (There are many more good pinks.)

*Pink Shades:* Fashion, coral-peach pink, a subtle and fascinating color and a superb rose in every way; Vogue, similar but a "louder" shade.

*Yellow:* Gold Cup is a new variety that may have lasting values.

*White:* Dagmar Späth; Summer Snow; Irene of Denmark, hardy and enduring, with blooms of especially attractive form. (A new variety, Ivory Fashion, will be a handsome addition if the plant proves reliable and enduring.)

*Other Colors:* Circus, variegated red, pink, yellow, orange and more attractive than the description suggests.

GRANDIFLORAS.  These are a new type of rose that is causing great excitement among rose fanciers. They are tall, vigorous plants with many blooms of hybrid tea form and quality and on individual stems, but they come in groups, much more often than singly, from the main canes. All the varieties are recent, but, so far, they have been of outstanding quality and the class is expanding faster and with greater promise than any of the older classes at this time.

### Varieties

*Medium Pink:* Queen Elizabeth, the rose that started the whole thing—it was so obviously good but wouldn't fit into any class as then constituted.

*Salmon-rose:* Montezuma, gives more constant bloom per plant than would have seemed possible before it appeared and holds its high-centered form to the end.

*Red:* Carrousel, at least as highly acclaimed as the others.

*Yellow:* Buccaneer, first classed as a tall hybrid tea but now usually classed as a grandiflora. More often than not the blooms come singly, but in size and other characteristics it fits in with the grandifloras.

Any of these can be used in a garden in the same way that tall hybrid teas or floribundas are used and they blend in well with both groups. They have enough plant growth to make a real mass effect in any garden. They appear to hold great possibilities as an everblooming tall shrub border in a small garden, along a boundary line, for instance, or to screen a parking or service area. Anyone now planning a new garden will do well to investigate these and newer varieties of the class. They could produce fresh, new planning ideas and their vigor promises well for use under what have been difficult conditions for roses; even if they are not as big as under ideal conditions, they should still be big enough to become a good substitute for older types.

MINIATURE ROSES.   These are exactly what the name implies: pygmy blooms on pygmy plants. A miniature rose takes up no more room than a johnny-jump-up and its usefulness in a tiny garden is obvious.

### Varieties

Red Imp, crimson; Robin, deep red; Midget, rose-red; Sweet

Fairy, pink, fragrant; Bo-Peep, light pink; Baby Gold Star, yellow; Cinderella, white, tinged pink; Pixie, white.

CLIMBING ROSES. Climbing roses are generally considered the easiest of all to grow. Hardy climbing stalwarts are: New Dawn, pink; Coral Dawn, coral pink; Blaze, red; Red Empress, large-flowered red; City of York, white; Golden Showers, yellow; Dr. C. J. Nicolas, pink. Dr. Nicolas and City of York are beautiful roses and tremendously floriferous, but they bloom only in June. The others repeat, especially in fall and especially if not allowed to make seeds. The climbing rose list is swelled continually by the addition of repeat-blooming climbing sports of hybrid teas and floribundas, as well as many other hardy varieties.

TREE ROSES. Tree roses or standard roses are those delightful bouquets surmounting a straight trunk about three feet high that lend themselves so admirably not only to formal garden planting but to woodcuts and book illustrations. They are a product of horticultural skill and cost more than a bare-root or plain potted rose. Any variety of rose can be budded to produce a tree rose. Tree roses are invaluable as accents in a bed of mixed roses, or in a panel of turf. They are wildly out of place in an informal garden.

OTHER ROSES. All of the foregoing are roses with which everyone is more or less familiar. They can be seen on millions of feet of Kodachrome film, in thousands of acres of exhibition plots and suburban lots, in the catalogs of the great rose nurseries of the land and even, alas, on the wrappers of deteriorated stock in chain stores that no experienced gardener would buy. They are the latest but not the last chapter in the dramatic story of the rose's evolution from a comparatively few species ancestors that have been around for thousands, some say millions, of years. They are not by any means the whole rose story, and it is important to remember that the old species roses and their earlier hybrids are not pale ghosts of the new types, but completely different, non-competitive plants, filling an entirely different niche of garden usefulness.

HYBRID PERPETUALS. The majority of species roses flower but once in a season, and had the historic encounter between the

Dukes of York and Lancaster, when one took a white rose as his badge and the other a red, occurred a few weeks earlier or later, it is safe to say that the Wars of the Roses would have been fought under another name. It was the desire of hybridists to overcome this weakness and obtain continuous flowering in roses hardy enough to grow outdoors in cold climates that produced the type known as hybrid perpetuals. These were important roses during a large part of the nineteenth century, occupying a comparable place in rose culture to today's hybrid tea; that is, they were the rose that excited the fancier and the rose for a romantic floral tribute.

Strictly speaking, there are no yellow hybrid perpetuals, though there is a borderline rose, Soleil d'Or, which has the growth habit of a hybrid perpetual and the color of the richest, ripest apricot you can imagine. Many of the hybrid perpetuals have wonderful fragrance and considerable color subtlety. The blooms are not pointed as in the hybrid tea, and they are often rather tight. Growth is stiff and a bit ungainly, so that it is not easy to tuck a hybrid perpetual into a mixed bed. They are splendid for loose espalier treatment against a fence or wall in a small garden. Another method is to peg the long canes on the ground, and though this produces an interesting and dramatic display at the height of bloom, it requires space and is most suited to gardens where there is room for specialty treatment.

All in all, the hybrid perpetuals have a quality of sturdiness, besides other less tangible traits that endear them to their admirers. Though their flowering is rarely perpetual in the strict sense of the word, perpetual is not a misnomer if one applies it to other qualities they possess; it is perhaps not too fanciful to say that there is in them a certain upright durability reminiscent of an oil painting of a Victorian ancestor.

VARIETIES. Hybrid perpetuals still popular today are: American Beauty, red; Henri Nevard, red; Baroness Rothschild, milky pink; Mrs. John Laing, pink; Frau Karl Druschki, white. Indeed, Frau Karl Druschki is still one of the outstanding white roses, robust and yet with great delicacy in its beautifully formed, paper white blooms.

SHRUB AND MISCELLANEOUS TYPE ROSES. Many of the old species roses make excellent shrubs, either in a mixed shrub planting or as specimen plants. A long-time favorite is *Rosa hugonis,* sometimes called Father Hugo's rose. Though the tiny, single yellow flowers are produced only in very early spring, its delicate fern-like foliage and graceful growth habit establish it as a worthy ornamental all season long. Under good growing conditions it may become very large. Harrison's Yellow is another popular spring-blooming shrub rose. Vanguard, a *Rosa rugosa* hybrid, may become almost a small tree, woody, picturesque, with salmon pink flowers. Another robust *R. rugosa* hybrid is Agnes, with pale amber fragrant flowers. Rugosa roses are excellent near the seashore and in northern climates. Some have repeat blooms all season. Pink Grootendorst has flowers more like a carnation than a rose.

The Fairy, a polyantha, makes a spreading mound up to three feet and more high and produces clusters of small pink flowers until frost. It survives sub-zero temperatures in a Connecticut garden I know, and performs excellently in New York City backyards—a supreme test. Another good everblooming low shrub type is Golden Wings, with large single yellow flowers.

HYBRID MUSKS. The hybrid musk roses are seldom included in popular lists, but they are extremely valuable for their ability to thrive in shady gardens. They are versatile, too, and some kinds will be equally happy pruned to bedding size, grown as a shrub, or allowed to scramble over walls, fences and banks. Pax, a creamy white, is larger flowered than most musks, very fragrant, and everblooming. It is delightful in a herb garden. Kathleen, the apple-blossom rose, is covered in spring with clusters of single white flowers and pink buds, and even in difficult situations will bloom intermittently all summer. Typically, it is everblooming. It is an altogether charming rose. I am not personally familiar with Belinda, a pink everblooming variety, but it usually receives the highest rating among musk roses. Hybrid musk roses are listed in the catalogs of nurseries specializing in old roses and can be safely shipped all over the country.

MOSS ROSES. Moss roses are often seen in old gardens and are still available for new ones, where they create their own aura of charm. They get their name from the conspicuous velvety green calyx that cups each bloom. They, too, will persist and even bloom in shade.

TEA ROSES.   Tea roses are tender in the north, but are much grown in Gulf-State gardens. They abound in delicate, subtle colors and the true tea rose perfume. There is languid grace in their growth and the way in which the flowers hang from the stem.

HOW TO CHOOSE AND BUY ROSES.   Climate and other conditions can so affect the performance of a rose that it becomes almost a different plant. For instance, in the part of Australia where I grew up the little Cecile Brunner or Sweetheart Rose was a lusty shrub, sometimes six feet high and wide in proportion. Since the propriety of choice is so dependent on geographical location, the safest way to make a selection is to consult local experience or obtain an American Rose Society regional list. The address of the American Rose Society is 4048 Roselea Place, Columbus, Ohio.

It is a great help if you can study actual blooming specimens of varieties you propose to buy. When you do this, consider not only the bloom but the foliage, too, for it varies a great deal; it may be strong and glossy as in Peace, or reddish as in Garnette, or light green as in Duquesa de Peneranda. The American Rose Society issues a voluminous list of rose gardens open to visitors.

The significance of a rose being an All-America winner is that such a rose has been tested in a number of places over a wide climatic range. Many excellent varieties that are not All-America winners perform with spectacular success in more limited areas, but these are kinds to order after you have talked to your neighbors or studied a regional list. Varieties that antedate the All-America tests have been time-tested, and those that have long continued to be widely grown are sure to be good.

It is good advice always to buy roses from a reliable nursery, and not to be seduced by an alluring wrapper or "bargain" prices. Roses are never expensive plants, compared with shrubs or trees, and it is plain stupid to try to save a few cents on anything so permanent. Not only may under-priced plants be the weakened discards of a florist's greenhouse, without the strength to give a respectable performance, but they may be the carriers of disease, or budded on root-stock unsuitable for your area, or damaged by improper handling. Roses ship well, and the big nurseries cater to the whole country, so there is no excuse for not buying the best stock available.

HOW TO USE ROSES. It should be obvious from the foregoing pages that the place of a rose in landscape work cannot easily be pinpointed. Since, however, bedding roses are by far the most popular kinds, the following notes should be taken to apply primarily to them.

Though it is conventional and usually most satisfactory to grow this type in a plot by themselves, or in a small specialty garden, designed for grouping varieties to the best advantage, this is not always possible in a small garden and one must devise ways of working them into borders and general plantings. One method is to use groups of three hybrid teas, all alike or of two varieties in a pleasing color and growth combination, and use each trio of plants as you would one shrub.

ORNAMENTS. When roses are grown in a special area, it is customary to introduce a piece of sculpture or some other kind of garden ornament, or a pool with a jet of water. This type of traditional rose garden can be perfectly delightful, but it is all too often marred by an insensitive choice of structural material. Roses make a lot of pattern, and their colors are brilliant. To combine them, therefore, with harsh colored brick, bright glazed pottery, and a lot of fussy ironwork, is a mistake. Mellow brick, grayish stone, or even old weathered wood, keep much better company with roses than material that is glaring and raw. One of the most beautiful substances for a rose garden ornament is lead; weathered bronze is also good, and soft-colored stone. Avoid concrete like the plague; even marble, if it is gleaming white, can be a little startling.

The paths in a rose garden are prettiest if they can be of grass, but brick and flagstone dry-laid can be very nice. A rigid brick or stone path set irrevocably in concrete is too hard.

The edging of the beds is important, too. Roses hold themselves above the ground, and a neat edging is imperative. Again, mellow brick or grayish stone usually looks best. Thin board edgings tend to look second rate, but an edging of weathered railway ties can be pleasing.

A rose garden should be at least partially enclosed, so that some of the beds can be against a background of shrubs or a wall. Roses are most effective if they are not the entire planting, but if some other material is used as a foil. Trees or shrubs with fine feathery foliage tend to be jittery; something dark and rich, or with strong clean planes, is most satisfactory. Ericaceous plants are unsuitable because they like a very acid soil and roses do not. In the North, yew is admirable. Boxwood is magnificent in a rose garden. *Euonymus japonica, Euonymus radicans vegetus,* and *Euonymus patens* are all appropriate. For an accompaniment to roses in California there is the lustrous English or cherry laurel *(Prunus laurocerasus),* also the true myrtle *(Myrtus communis).*

Whatever enclosure is used for a rose garden should not be of a kind to exclude the air circulation which roses must have.

COLOR HARMONY.    The range of color in the newer roses and their prolonged blooming have greatly increased their usefulness in a garden. For instance, an expanse of harsh red brick may need a cooling foreground of white. A bank of azaleas will serve only briefly, as will most flowering shrubs, but a planting of white floribundas will bloom freely all summer. The warm tones of a pink-apricot variety such as Helen Traubel will do wonders for a chilly bit of concrete or light gray stone; the dark gray of slate will heighten the intensity of a bright pink rose and itself be enhanced.

A rose is a dominant plant that will not be ignored or overlooked. It is important, therefore, to choose colors that are comfortable not only with other plants but with outdoor furniture and anything within the same range of vision. Be especially careful of brilliant varieties, such as floribundas that contain a lot of orange; they can create color splendor or havoc, depending on where and how they are used.

Study differences in plant height and growth form so that low kinds can be used to "face down" taller plants. Some tall growers can be kept low by pruning, but don't do this impulsively; there are vigorous growers such as Peace that can be discouraged and even injured by this treatment. Instead, use the vigorous varieties where bulk and height are an asset, such as to flank garden steps, as "anchor men" in a bed, for turning corners, and so on. Rhythm can be achieved throughout the length of a very long rose border of bedding roses by introducing, at repeated intervals and the ends, a strikingly different variety (perhaps the shrubby, cluster-flowered The Fairy, for instance). This will provide bay effects between the other types in the bed. Except for the extremely shrubby type roses, a single row of roses is usually too thin; use a staggered double row, even for short lengths, and intermix bulky and upright-growing varieties to give solidity to the whole planting.

ROSE CULTURE.   Many excellent books on rose culture are available; two are included in the reference list at the end of this book. Most nurseries give concise directions for planting with every rose order. Cultural practice varies somewhat with climate, so it is always wise to supplement reading with observation of your neighbor's methods; a successful grower rarely minds being questioned.

## Bulbs

Bulbs, in the minds of thousands of northern home gardeners, are tulips, daffodils and crocuses. And with just these three kinds of bulbs, the garden is brought to life in spring with a burst of color that is tropical in its splendor.

Actually, of course, tulips, daffodils and crocuses are but three members of a big group of plants, native to many different climates and fulfilling many different purposes in the garden, but all having one thing in common: the buds from which the plants grow are contained in a mass of food storage tissue from which the young growing plant draws nourishment. When flowering is finished, nutriment from the leaves replenishes the storage tissue. This is why, unless bulbs are to be treated strictly as annuals and replaced each year, the foliage should never be cut but should be allowed to ripen and die slowly while attached to the bulb.

A bulb, therefore, whether it is a true bulb (daffodil, lily, crinum, dog's-tooth violet, snowdrop, hyacinth, allium, bulbous iris), or a corm (crocus, gladiolus, brodiaea, meadow saffron, mariposa lily, montbretia, ixia) is a plant that appears once a year above ground, flowers briefly, and returns to a period of subterranean dormancy.

Other plants sometimes loosely called bulbs store food in tuberous roots (daylilies, dahlias), or rhizomes (bearded iris, calla lilies), but not all members of these classes vanish from the bed when flowering is finished and are as often listed as a type of perennial or in a class by themselves as under the heading of bulbs.

CULTURE. The purpose of the plant notes in this book is primarily to present plants to beginner gardeners as a means of expressing garden design, and to leave their botanical differences and specific horticultural needs to writers on specialized subjects. The following notes therefore should be read as a general guide to growing bulbs that are in common use:

1. Plant in well-drained soil. If the bulb spends its dormant period in water-logged soil, it will rot. If there is the slightest tendency for the soil to be over-moist, make the hole larger than the size of the bulb requires and mix sand with the soil under the bulb.

2. Plant in ordinary good garden soil, using plenty of organic material. If stable manure is used, be sure that it is well rotted. Bone meal is considered one of the best fertilizers for bulbs and many growers mix a sprinkling with the soil at the bottom of each hole when planting.

3. A general rule is that the soil covering should be equal in depth to three times the diameter of the bulb, but some latitude is permissible and there is even some difference of opinion, especially about tulips. If planting is shallow in cold climates there is danger of winter heaving and of too-early growth above ground in spring. It is better to err on the side of deep rather than shallow planting.

4. Press the bulb firmly into the soil. It will be difficult to do this if the hole tapers to a point at the bottom; make it broad enough at the base for the bulb to sit firmly on the ground.

5. Cover with a mulch *after* the ground has frozen. The purpose of this is not to keep the bulbs warm but to prevent the ground from thawing and heaving. Soft leaves are not a good mulch because they tend to pack down and make a soggy mass. Remove the mulch in early spring, since if the leaves have to grow up through a mulch they will be yellow and spindly.

HOW TO USE BULBS. How bulbs are used and what bulbs to select depends, of course, on the kind of garden they are to adorn. Since tulips, daffodils *(Narcissus)*, crocuses, and various other small spring-flowering bulbs are by far the most popular in any climate where they can be grown, let us give them priority of attention.

DAFFODILS. Daffodil is merely the English word for narcissus. According to the Oxford Dictionary, it is a variant of the word "affodil" and became a part of the English language in the sixteenth century. Apparently the origin of the "d" is obscure, but whoever attached it to "affodil" made a much prettier word. In the trade, "daffodil" is often limited to certain kinds of narcissus, but strictly daffodil and narcissus are synonyms, one English and the other Latin.

Daffodils need to make some root growth in fall, and for this reason it is more serious to delay their planting than it is to be tardy with tulips. September and early October is the time to plant daffodils.

## Kinds of Daffodils

Daffodils are classified according to the size of the trumpet or cup, whether the petals are white or yellow or reflexed, whether there is red in the cup, and whether the flowers are single or double, and borne singly or in clusters. To get an idea of the tremendous variety of daffodils as individual plants go to a flower show and study the exhibits. This is a special way of looking at daffodils, and all-important to some people. To other, daffodils are simply the flowers that bring sheets and splashes of yellow to the garden, briefly but vividly, before the tulip parade.

Even in a very small garden, daffodils are most effective grown in clumps or naturalized in drifts. Planted in clumps, they should be carefully placed, so that their color is distributed and is against a background, such as evergreens or a fence or a wall of grayish stone.

The big trumpet kinds make the strongest accents; the more delicate types are for finer work. Some of the dwarf daffodils, such as the charming hoop-petticoats, are really in the class of small bulbs and will be lost if they are planted to face up a shrub. They are best in a rock garden, or to complete miniature flower pictures.

## Naturalizing

Though the phrase "naturalized daffodils" usually conjures up a vision of a big expanse of undulating land, perhaps sloping down to a lake or stream, where drifts of yellow pattern the grass, in a small garden daffodils may be scattered casually under one or two deciduous trees, or in front of and between shrubs bordering a lawn or walk. Throw or drop the bulbs in handfuls and plant them where they fall. When daffodils are planted in this way, the dying foliage is much less unsightly than when bulbs are fading in a border; one is not bothered by it any more than one is bothered by the rhythm of life and decay in the woods. In a position where the dead leaves will be troublesome, varieties such as Mount Hood with abnormally wide strap-like leaves should be avoided. Use narrower-leafed varieties and plant them where other material will grow up and make a screen. Ferns are ideal.

Under most conditions, daffodils will flower year after year in the same place. After two or three years the flowers decrease in size, and the correct horticultural practice is to "lift" the bulbs, cure them, and separate them, but many home gardeners prefer simply to make fresh plantings when the old stock is petering out, or to add a few new ones each year.

Special mixtures are sold for naturalizing; these are tough, hardy kinds which are good for difficult situations such as northern city gardens or when the grower is a little casual about horticultural niceties. How close together to plant daffodils depends on the effect you want to get.

TULIPS. Tulips are wonderful as stabs of color in strategic spots, and they are enormously effective in clumps in a mixed border. They, like daffodils, are not at their best in a small garden if they are massed solidly in beds. Nor should they be planted in a hard straight line.

This may be an unjustified opinion, but, for me, daffodils are not for a mixed border any more than tulips are suitable for naturalizing. There is something formal about a tulip, and something wild and wanton about a daffodil. For this reason, tulips are excellent in the vicinity of classical sculpture, while daffodils keep better company with weathered rock.

When tulips are planted informally in a border, they will look spotty if nothing else is very far advanced. A backing of shrubs helps, and an interplanting of pansies and annuals such as phlox, petunias, or verbena in pastel shades. Arabis (rock cress), a perennial, is one of the most delightful plants to flower along with tulips and makes a splendid border subject.

## Kinds of Tulips

The classification of tulips is rather confusing, and really the only important thing for the beginner gardener to know is that there are early and late kinds, low-growing and tall-growing, single and double.

Among the early kinds there is none more spectacular than Red Emperor, a huge vermilion-scarlet tulip with a splotch of purple inside the cup at the base and conspicuous black stamens. Where I live it flowers about the middle of April, before the early single tulips. Red Emperor is a Fosteriana tulip.

The early single and early double-flowering tulips are not as tall as the May-flowering kinds. The singles open before the doubles, so they are best mixed. One of the best early singles is de Wet, an orange tulip; it is also exceptionally long lasting. A popular early double is Peach Blossom, a soft and lovely pink.

The tall May-flowering tulips include the kinds known as cottage, Darwin, breeder, parrot, and lily-flowering. Everyone has his favorites among them, and the best way to discover yours is to get a catalog, make a list of different colors, and then wait for results. By the second year you will know which ones you like and which were a disappointment.

Correct horticultural practice is to lift tulip bulbs every year, cure them, separate them and replant. The average gardener prefers to wait two or three years and then replace them, or to keep adding new ones each year so that he is not entirely dependent on an old planting. In many city gardens it is common practice to treat tulips as annuals and plant afresh every fall.

THE SMALL BULBS. The little bulbs that do not always wait until the snow has melted before they flower, and continue through early spring to carpet the ground with yellow, white,

purple, and intense shades of blue, are a flower world in miniature. Most of the common sorts are among the easiest plants to
grow. The bulbs are so tiny that a hundred and more can be
planted in no time at all, and from then on there is nothing to
do except keep the ground moist during fall, mulch them lightly
after freezing, and wait for spring; then leave them alone and
wait for them to flower again, often in greater quantity, the
following year.

This group of bulbs includes crocuses, squills and bluebells
(*Scilla*), chionodoxas, grape hyacinths, fritillarias, snowflakes,
snowdrops, and many more. For the connoisseur, each of these
names is a key word for a host of varieties; these have been discussed lovingly and at length by writers who scour the world
for new forms and keep minute records of their performance.
No garden is too small to contain the little bulbs, and it is hard
to imagine a gardener too feeble to handle them.

They are plants for rock gardens, between stepping stones,
in groupings against a low wall, and, perhaps best of all, in
drifts around the edges of a tiny lawn. Generally, their grass-
like leaves fade inconspicuously.

Compared with other colors, there are not many truly blue
flowers, but blue varieties of scilla, chionodoxa and grape hyacinth (*Muscari*) usher in the season with the blue of the heavens. (Indeed, the gardener searching for a blue flower is well
advised to consider the bulbs.) Grape hyacinths flower over a
longer period than scillas, and for this reason are better than
scillas for drift effects. On the other hand, since they increase
rapidly, they are sometimes too aggressive for a rock planting.

ALLIUMS.   Judging from the difficulty of finding catalogs that
list them in variety, the alliums are not widely planted, but they
are a deserving group of June and July flowering bulbs of remarkably easy culture. *Allium caeruleum* (*A. azureum*) is particularly noteworthy because of its lovely sky-blue color. The
flowers are in a rounded lacy cluster on a slender two foot
stem and may last for three weeks. They are charming in a bed
of pink roses.

Other species such as *A. zebdanense* and *A. neapolitanum*,
have flowers like white lace. *A. giganteum* produces a lilac ball

on a tall stem (over three feet) and, with its large basal leaves, is a dramatic accent plant.

A number of alliums are native to California and are described by Lester Rowntree in *Hardy Californians*. Unfortunately, the smell of the leaves if handled too fondly betrays the fact that alliums are, after all, onions.

LILIES. Lilies require a more specialized discussion than the bulbs mentioned above and it cannot be attempted here. It is true that there are casual and even difficult gardens in which lilies grow with the greatest abandon, but you may be sure that it is because they happen to be the right lilies in the right place. The wrong lilies in the wrong place can only be a disappointment, and that is why it is dangerous to make general statements about lily culture except to refer the reader to a book in which space permits a thorough discussion with qualifying remarks about the different varieties. *The Complete Book of Bulbs* by F. F. Rockwell and Esther C. Grayson is such a book.

## Lilies in the Wild

Residents of the Pacific Coast are fortunate in that they can see, in the mountain meadows of their own home territory, native lilies which have become established in gardens around the world. Note their companions, and their physical environment, and you will get the best possible clue as to how to treat them in your garden.

Apart, too, from the practical value of studying garden plants in their wild state, to do so is a spur to the imagination. One of the indelible pictures I carry is a grassy hillside on an island off the coast of Formosa. The grass was silver when the wind rippled it and lilies were strewn among it like pink poppies in a field of corn.

## Lilies in the Garden

What I have said about lilies suggests, perhaps, that they are plants for wild places, but, actually, no plant lends itself more to formal and manicured gardens. Tall or short, white or vividly spotted and splashed with color, lilies possess at once a dewy freshness and an elegance that makes them invaluable for perfecting a certain kind of garden picture.

White varieties are wonderful in a rose garden. Pink kinds make perfect companions for delphiniums. The orange lilies are dramatic accents. Lilies are superb against a background of rich evergreens or old stone. For all their fastidious restraint, lilies are dominant plants and the gardener should ponder well the way he proposes to use them.

MISCELLANEOUS BULBS.   Many half-hardy and tender bulbous plants that in the North must be wintered indoors are good general garden and border plants in warm spots of the country. *Calochortus* (mariposa lily, star tulip, globe tulip) and *Brodiaea* are native to the West Coast and anyone wanting to read about the many species of these two bulbs in their natural environment is referred to the chapter on wild bulbs in Lester Rowntree's *Hardy Californians. Brodiaea laxa* (lavender blue) and *B. coronaria* (purple) are hardy in sheltered locations in the East.

Other important bulbous plants in this huge tender and half-hardy group come from South Africa and include the vivid and useful yellow-orange montbretia *(Tritonia)* and the grass-like ixias. Catalog descriptions of ixias always sound rather dull, but in Australia as a child I was familiar with an ixia that was the color of a tropical sea.

The fancy-leaf caladiums and the lush elephant-ear *(Colocasia)* are tender tuberous plants. Both are popular in the North for a rather artificial type of gardening; elephant-ear has much to commend it where there is space for it, but fancy-leaf caladiums often look synthetic. In hot climates, of course, where they are at home, it is a different story.

There is no doubt that some plants that have been yanked out of the wild and settled down with remarkable content in new homes have never quite found themselves as garden plants. Such a one, I always think, is the calla-lily *(Zantedeschia),* which, incidentally, is not a lily at all. It is a native of the tropics and is immensely popular for flower arrangements. It is sometimes recommended for pool-side planting in the North.

The list of interesting and beautiful bulbs could go on and on. I hope enough has been said to show that they have a wide and varied use in the garden and, as with every other plant, the only way to know anything about them is to grow them.

# LIBRARY

Every gardener should have a small reference library. If I had to limit myself to one book, it would be Taylor's *Encyclopedia of Gardening* (Houghton Mifflin Co., Boston, Mass.) It contains sections on every part of the country, comprehensive plant lists, diagrams, and concise information about specific plants and cultural practice. The cost is $15.00, but it can save a gardener many times that sum.

### Regional

*Southwest Gardening,* by Rosalie Doolittle (University of New Mexico Press, Albuquerque, N. M.)

*The Southern Gardener,* by Mary B. Stewart (Robert L. Crager Co., New Orleans, La.)

*Sunset Western Garden Book* (Lane Book Co., Menlo Park, Calif.)

*The Green Thumb Magazine,* a periodical for gardeners in the Rocky Mountain area published by the Colorado Forestry and Horticultural Association, 909 York Street, Denver 6, Colo.

*Your Garden in the South,* by Hamilton Mason (D. Van Nostrand Company, Inc., Princeton, N. J.)

### Construction

*Walks and Paths, Driveways, Steps, Curbs and Edgings,* by R. R. Hawkins and C. H. Abbe (D. Van Nostrand Company, Inc.)

*Designs for Outdoor Living,* by John Burton Brimer (Doubleday & Company, Inc., New York.)

*Mosaics—Design, Construction and Assembly,* by Robert Williamson (Hearthside Press, Inc., New York.)

## Design

*Garden Design,* by Sylvia Crowe (Hearthside Press, Inc.)

## Specialty Books

*Flowering Trees of the World for Tropics and Warm Climates,* by Edwin A. Menninger (Hearthside Press, Inc.)

*The Gardener's Bug Book,* by Cynthia Westcott (Doubleday & Co., Inc.)

*Garden Enemies,* by Cynthia Westcott (D. Van Nostrand Company, Inc.)

*Rose Growing Simplified,* by John Milton (Hearthside Press, Inc.)

*Anyone Can Grow Roses,* by Cynthia Westcott (D. Van Nostrand Company, Inc.)

*Gardening in the Shade,* by H. K. Morse (Charles Scribner's Sons, New York.)

*The Complete Book of Bulbs,* by F. F. Rockwell and Esther C. Grayson (Doubleday & Company, Inc.)

*Daffodils, Outdoors and In,* by Carey E. Quinn (Hearthside Press, Inc.)

*Peonies, Outdoors and In,* by Arno and Irene Nehrling (Hearthside Press, Inc.)

*100 Finest Trees and Shrubs,* Handbook No. 25, Brooklyn Botanic Garden, 1000 Washington Avenue, Brooklyn 25, New York.

*Handbook on Vines,* Brooklyn Botanic Garden.

*T. H. Everett's Lawns and Landscaping Handbook* (Fawcett Book No. 302, Fawcett Publications, Inc., Greenwich, Conn.)

The United States Department of Agriculture publishes leaflets on a variety of garden subjects, including construction. Write to the U.S.D.A. in Washington, D.C., for a list of titles. The cost of the pamphlets is nominal.

Most State colleges have an agricultural extension service from which advice can be obtained on local gardening problems. Information is also available from county agents.

# INDEX

# INDEX